The Moorland Balance

The Science Behind Grouse Shooting
and Moorland Management

Second Edition

Game & Wildlife
CONSERVATION TRUST

First published in Great Britain in 2019 by
Game & Wildlife Conservation Trading Ltd
Burgate Manor, Fordingbridge SP6 1EF
www.gwct.org.uk

A catalogue record for this book is available from
the British Library.

First printed September 2019

ISBN: 978 1 901369 33 5

Written by Jennifer Brewin and edited by Dave Baines,
Joe Dimbleby, Nick Hesford, Sonja Ludwig, David Newborn,
Jonathan Reynolds, Adam Smith and Sian Whitehead.

Designed and typeset in Plantin MT Pro
by James Swyer.

Front cover © Tarquin Millington-Drake
Inside front cover © Lizzie Shepherd

Special thanks to Tarquin Millington-Drake for allowing the
use of his photography at no cost.

Contents

Foreword

Since I began my political career 43 years ago management of the uplands has changed dramatically. Financial incentives had previously led to large areas of heather moorland being lost to overgrazing and afforestation. In the years that followed, Government and conservation bodies made great efforts to reverse that loss. In more recent times, it seems support for heather moorland restoration has waned in some quarters with 'rewilding' and tree planting now in fashion. Yet through all these changes, grouse management has remained a constant, continuing to preserve our remaining heather-clad uplands as it has done for decades.

This updated and extended edition of The Moorland Balance explains how grouse management has successfully protected this much-loved habitat. It is entirely based on scientific research and contains references to more than 160 peer-reviewed papers from a wide range of sources. Where there is a gap in knowledge it recognises that fact and where there is a controversial issue, particularly in the case of the illegal killing of raptors, it doesn't shy away from addressing it.

At the same time in an effort to move the debate around grouse management onto a more rational, less adversarial footing, it demonstrates how science challenges many of the false claims made in the media. Increasingly, criticisms of grouse shooting have little basis in fact. For example, a repeated allegation is that moorlands were and still are drained by grouse managers. In fact, the opposite is true. Grouse managers have no interest in draining moors, and paradoxically they have done a huge amount to reverse the damage by filling in the ditches (see page 37).

Another fact that gets overlooked is that the UK's heather moorland and its unique collections of flora and fauna are recognised as globally important habitat. As well as being internationally significant, heather and the red grouse that depend on it are still highly valued as part of the UK's cultural heritage and many moors are designated Special Protection Areas for the species they support. This book refers to evidence that were driven grouse management to end, either through draconian licencing or an outright ban, the knock-on effect would likely be the loss of our precious heather moorland and the rare wildlife and rural communities it sustains. Anyone who reads these pages will make up their own minds about such an outcome, but they will start from the basis of scientific fact rather than ideological opinion.

Sir Jim Paice

Left: © Tarquin Millington-Drake; Above: © Matt Limb

1. Grouse Shooting

Grouse shooting in the UK occurs in two main forms: driven shooting and walked-up, often over dogs. Driven shooting typically requires higher grouse densities, and this needs more effective management. The scale and impact of this management is the issue which provokes much of the debate around grouse shooting. This chapter describes grouse shooting and introduces the management techniques used.

What are grouse and where are they found?

There are four species of grouse in Britain: red grouse, black grouse, capercaillie and ptarmigan. The red grouse population is estimated to be 230,000 pairs[1], and it is one of this country's few endemic sub-species, meaning that they are only found in the British Isles. They inhabit heather moorland including areas of both blanket bog and upland heath.

The black grouse population is estimated to be 5,100 males UK-wide[1]. They are found on the moorland fringe and use hill-edge woodlands of both conifer and deciduous species. There are fewer than 2,000 capercaillie in a handful of pine-dominated Scottish woodlands[1]. Ptarmigan live above 800m and like capercaillie are also only found in Scotland. Grouse populations tend to fluctuate in size over the years and in relation to management, so these figures are an estimate.

Species	Population status	Population estimate	UK conservation trend
Red grouse	230,000 pairs	Fluctuating	Amber listed
Black grouse	5,100 males	Severe decline	Red listed
Capercaillie	1,300 individuals (800-1,900)	Severe decline	Red listed
Ptarmigan	2,000-15,000 pairs	Unknown (range stable)	Green listed

The number and trends of grouse species in the UK, based on figures from Birds of Conservation Concern 4[2], Population estimates of birds in Great Britain and the UK[1] and Birdlife International's Datazone.

Which grouse are shot on driven grouse moors?

Red grouse. They are regarded as the paragon of gamebirds because their speed and agility provides challenging shooting.

Are red grouse wild birds?

Yes. Red grouse are entirely wild, unlike many pheasant or partridge shoots, which rely on rearing and releasing birds. Although attempts have been made to rear red grouse, this has not been successful. Grouse management aims to maintain moorland in a high-quality condition for these wild birds.

What is driven shooting?

Red grouse, pheasants and partridges are 'driven', where birds are flushed by a line of beaters and fly over the people shooting (the 'Guns'), who are stationary in a line. On grouse moors they typically stand in a line of 'butts' – specially constructed shooting positions often built out of wood, stone and turf. Red grouse are also shot 'walked-up', where the participants walk across the moorland, flushing birds as they go, often using dogs to find grouse.

Grouse butts are fundamental to driven shooting and are a cultural aspect of some UK moorlands © Steve Jackson

How are driven grouse moors managed?

Moorland management for driven grouse shooting includes controlling generalist predators such as crows and foxes, heather management, often by grazing and prescribed burning, and disease control. These topics are discussed in their own chapters through this book.

Are there benefits of driven grouse shooting over walked-up shooting?

Aiming to produce enough grouse to drive means moors have to invest more in staff, time and equipment than where walked up shooting is the only aim. This allows more consistent, effective predator and disease control, along with habitat management. This greater investment in management has benefits for other moorland wildlife, such as species of ground-nesting birds[3-6], and for habitats and the environment (see chapter 2 on conservation). A driven grouse shoot can make this additional investment because the economic returns for driven shooting are much greater than for walked-up shooting[7] (see chapter 10 for more information about the economics of grouse moors).

Are there negative impacts?

If the law and best practice guidelines are not followed, there can be negative impacts from practices such as illegal raptor killing or inappropriate burning. Some impacts can be avoided by adherence to the law and best practice guidance, which uses the best available knowledge to avoid or reduce these to acceptable levels. These issues will be discussed throughout the book.

Are the benefits widely recognised?

Yes. In response to the last petition to ban driven grouse shooting in 2016, the UK government released a statement recognising that: "When carried out in accordance with the law, grouse shooting for sport is a legitimate activity and in addition to its significant economic contribution, providing jobs and investment in some of our most remote areas, it can offer important benefits for wildlife and habitat conservation"[8].

Managed heather moorland has been recognised as iconic and archetypal[9], and the Scottish Cabinet Secretary for Environment, Climate Change and Land Reform has expressed a wish to "... ensure that grouse moor management continues to contribute to the rural economy..."[10].

In driven shooting, beaters flush the birds over the waiting Guns. © *Matt Limb*

Above and left © Tarquin Millington-Drake

2. Grouse moors and conservation

Although sometimes imagined as an open, uniform expanse of moorland, the UK's uplands actually consist of a variety of environments and habitats, supporting different activities across the landscape. Farming, forestry, grouse moors, deer management, wind farms and nature reserves are all found in the uplands. These different areas support different communities of plant and animal species, but fragmentation of open moorland environments by these other land uses can be detrimental to some species.

Although grouse moor management is felt by some to be controversial, its importance to certain habitats and species means that its role within the mix of land uses is of recognised conservation value. This chapter looks at the contribution of grouse moor management to conservation in the UK.

Where are grouse moors found?

On heather moorland in the UK uplands; mainly concentrated in the hills of central and eastern Scotland, the Pennines and North York Moors. Grouse moors often occur on peat soils; either deep peat, which can be blanket bog (see chapter 3), or shallow peat and mineral soils, which are on heathland areas. Grouse eat the young shoots of heather plants, so heather management, usually by controlled burning, is undertaken to encourage new growth. A mix of young and older heather provides both good food quality and cover for nesting.

Why is our heather moorland important?

No other country has extensive heather uplands equivalent to those in the UK. Most other heather areas are lowland or coastal, leaving the UK responsible for 75% of the world's heather moorland[11]. For this reason, the 1992 Rio Convention on Biodiversity recognised the global importance of UK heather moorland[12].

Heather-dominated moorland supports groups or 'communities' of plants growing together that are either only found in the UK, or are found more abundantly here than elsewhere in the world[13]. These communities are different to those found under other land uses such as commercial forestry, so grouse moor management can help increase overall biodiversity in the uplands. They include species of berry, grass, sedge and mosses such as *Sphagnum*, which together define habitats that are listed under the EU's Conservation of Natural Habitats and of Wild Flora and Fauna Directive.

Although invertebrate diversity tends to be relatively low when compared with other habitats, rare species are associated with moorland, including moths, bees, butterflies, various money spider species, craneflies, and ground beetles[14]. For example, the bilberry or mountain bumblebee is only found in bilberry-rich moorlands with heather, which provides nectar late in the summer and protection from the weather[15]. Butterflies and moths tend to be more diverse and abundant on moorland areas when heather is older, compared to recently burnt areas[16].

The moorland environment also supports a collection of birds (an "assemblage"), which contains many species of European or international importance, for example red grouse, golden plover, curlew, lapwing and short eared owl[13,17]. Although not their sole habitat, many of these species are found in greater numbers and may breed more successfully on managed grouse moors[3–5].

The UK is responsible for 75% of the world's heather moorland. © GWCT

Overall, the number of species of plants or animals found on heather moorland can be fairly low, but those species which thrive are often uncommon, specialist species not found elsewhere, meaning that maintaining heather moorland is important for their conservation.

Does grouse moor management help conserve heather moorland?

Yes. Until the early 2000s, heather cover was falling sharply in the UK, generally as a result of overgrazing and commercial forestry plantations. However, a GWCT study showed that management for driven grouse shooting slows the loss of heather from our landscape. Between the 1940s and 1980s, moors that stopped grouse shooting lost 41% of their heather cover, while moors retaining shooting lost only 24%[18]. Historically, a landowner's commitment to grouse management may have dissuaded them from converting moors to other land uses such as forestry or agriculture[18] (see chapter 9 for more on alternative moorland uses).

Many designations in the uplands were originally made because of the habitats and species on moorland, which can be supported by grouse management. Some of the best examples of heather moorland in the UK are designated as Sites of Special Scientific Interest (SSSIs) and 'Natura' sites – Special Protection Areas (SPA) and Special Areas of Conservation (SAC) – in recognition of their importance. In England, 74% of upland SPAs are managed as grouse moors[19]. However, on some grouse moors inappropriate burning or the lack of agreed heather management plans have led to the classification of the site as being in unfavourable condition.

Can preserving heather moorland contribute to carbon storage?

Yes. Peatlands store around 30% of the world's soil carbon[20] and some areas of moorland have layers of deep peat under the surface, which help lock up carbon. Experiments studying global warming show that moorland where heather is the dominant plant species has the potential to store more carbon than moorland with grass cover[21]. The role of grouse moor management techniques and how they may affect carbon storage is an important ongoing area of research (see page 28 for further information on carbon storage).

Can lost heather be recovered?

Yes, with a long-term commitment to restoration. There have been a number of heather recovery projects in the Peak District and the Langholm Moor Demonstration Project used a combination of reduced sheep grazing with a heather management strategy that included burning, cutting and reseeding. These approaches improved both overall heather cover by 10%, and the area of heather-dominated vegetation by 30%[22].

A recent study showed range contraction for golden plover and other wader species was smallest where grouse shooting was retained and greatest where it had disappeared completely. © Tarquin Millington-Drake

11

Which bird species thrive on moors keepered for grouse?

Some birds occur at higher densities and breed more successfully on moors managed for red grouse than on other moorland. These include globally threatened species such as curlew and merlin but also red grouse and golden plover, with lapwing and black grouse on the fringes of grouse moors[3,23,24]. More than half of English uplands are managed as grouse moors, mostly concentrated in the North Pennines, the South Pennines and the North York Moors. These three areas have all been designated as Special Protection Areas (SPA) mostly on the basis of their substantial numbers of breeding waders, merlin or hen harrier[7].

What is the evidence for this?

As well as red grouse, there is strong evidence that grouse moor management is beneficial for a group of wader species, including curlew, golden plover and lapwing. Several studies have found this:

- The GWCT's Upland Predation Experiment looked at the effect of predator control, which is one aspect of grouse moor management, and found that lapwing, golden plover, curlew, red grouse and meadow pipit bred on average three times more successfully when predator control was performed, compared to the same moorland when predators were not controlled. As a result, breeding numbers increased in subsequent years, but in the absence of predator control, they declined[5].
- Results from the Langholm Moor Demonstration Project showed that restoring grouse management after eight years was beneficial for three wader species. Overall, curlew numbers rose by 10% per year on average, golden plover by 16% and snipe by 21%. However, lapwing numbers remained low[6].
- A recent GWCT analysis of upland bird species trends

in south-west Scotland found declines in several upland bird species, including red and black grouse, golden plover, lapwing and curlew, and these are generally attributed to large-scale changes in land use, including afforestation, more intensive farming and reductions in grouse moor management[25].

- An analysis of the status of grouse management in the north of England, the Scottish mainland, Wales and south-west of England showed that range contraction for curlew, golden plover, lapwing and dunlin was smallest where grouse shooting was retained and greatest where it had disappeared completely[26].
- Another study which looked at the change in bird numbers when moorland management stopped also found that some species of moorland bird declined when grouse moor management ended[27].

On the other hand, there is also evidence that some species including meadow pipit and skylark occur at lower densities on grouse moors because they prefer a grassier environment[28]. The story for meadow pipits is unclear, as certain studies find benefits from aspects of keepering[5] (see above). There are also lower than expected densities of birds of prey (raptors), including golden eagle[29,30], hen harrier[31] and peregrine[32] on grouse moors, due their illegal killing by gamekeepers (see chapter 7).

Can grouse moor management be good for birds of prey?

In the absence of illegal killing, it has long been felt that grouse moors could provide good habitat for raptors[33]. Studies of raptors identify that grouse moors have the potential to benefit their conservation by supporting large amounts of prey[34,35]. One study showed that hen harrier breeding success was higher when a moor was keepered, likely as a result of reduced predation on hen harrier eggs and chicks, particularly by foxes, which was found to be the main cause of breeding failure[36]. Analysis of grouse moor management in the absence of illegal killing at Langholm moor showed that hen harrier numbers were higher during periods of keepering[37] (see page 62).

Hen harriers may also benefit from the vegetation management carried out on grouse moors, as heather is their preferred upland nesting habitat and grouse moors are managed to retain heather[18]. However, we must recognise that these findings are largely from Langholm Moor, where raptors were not illegally controlled by gamekeepers. Elsewhere, illegal killing of raptors still occurs and grouse moor management impacts on the numbers and breeding success of several species[31,38].

Merlin have been shown to breed successfully on grouse moors.
© *Tarquin Millington-Drake*

Merlin are predominantly ground-nesting birds of prey, so are also likely to benefit from the predator management carried out on grouse moors, especially fox control[25,39]. Higher breeding success of meadow pipits when predators are controlled may also help increase food supplies for merlin[5]. A recent unpublished report divided England into 1km squares and looked for evidence of breeding merlin. These squares were then correlated with a map of known grouse moors to see where merlin are breeding. 80% of squares containing merlin were found to be on grouse moors, with only 20% on non-grouse moors.

Associations such as this are not proof of a benefit, but this work adds to the other evidence suggesting that grouse moor management may help provide a suitable nesting environment for these raptors[40]. Some moorland keepers in northern England work co-operatively with local raptor study groups, helping to find nests and ensure that merlin broods are ringed. Many keepers are proud of the merlins their moors support and acknowledge that merlin pose little threat to their grouse.

Do curlew benefit from grouse moor management?

Studies suggest curlew thrive on grouse moors. This is important because a paper published in 2015 stated that the curlew should be considered the UK's species of highest conservation concern[41], having declined rapidly both nationally (50% in the past 25 years[2]) and internationally (up to 30% in the past 25 years[42]).

Curlew have declined by 50% in the past 25 years. © GWCT

Several studies have found an association between areas managed for grouse and a higher density of curlew, suggesting that the techniques used there may benefit them. The Upland Predation Experiment, carried out in Northumberland, showed that predator control can increase curlew breeding success threefold[5]. The importance of upland breeding areas for the survival of curlew is likely to increase, as other traditional breeding areas such as lowland wetlands can no longer sustain wader populations. Between 1982 and 2002 the number of curlew breeding on lowland grassland in England and Wales dropped by 39%[43,44].

Why is grouse moor management important for black grouse?

The last estimate of black grouse numbers in the whole of Britain was 5,078 males in 2005 with the population centred on a few key upland areas of Scotland, northern England and North Wales[45]. In England black grouse are confined to the North Pennines, where 90% of the remaining population lives on the edges of moors keepered for red grouse[46]. Black grouse are birds of the upland fringe rather than the moor exclusively. They use a range of different habitats and depend on these being present near each other across a landscape. These including rough pasture, upland grasses and broad-leaved copses.

Research in the UK indicates black grouse are vulnerable to predation by foxes, stoats and raptors, whilst high densities of livestock can reduce essential cover and render them more at risk from those predators[47]. For this reason, land management measures associated with upland farms on the fringes of grouse moors, including predator control and grazing restrictions, can benefit black grouse breeding success and overall survival[46,47]. A GWCT study in Wales found that black grouse declined in parallel with the loss of driven grouse shooting. Since this report was published, the authors have predicted black grouse may become restricted to the only driven grouse moor in North Wales within the next 10 years. It is estimated that this moor already supports more than 85% of the Welsh black grouse population[27].

How are black grouse populations faring in the UK?

Black grouse were once widespread throughout the UK, with their range extending even to Hampshire as late as the 1930s. Since then the red-listed species has undergone a dramatic decline. In 1998 there were only 773 displaying males left[45] in England. This figure temporarily recovered to 1,437 in 2014. The species remains severely threatened in England due to its small population and limited range. Numbers fluctuate around 1,000 males, and are affected by weather including rainfall in June, which influences breeding success[48] and snow depth and duration which affects winter survival[49].

Black grouse are severely threatened in England due to the small population and limited range. © *David Kjaer*

Black grouse are more abundant in northern Scotland, benefiting from an array of suitable semi-natural habitats including moorland and native woodland connected to each other across the landscape. Numbers are now very low south of the Glasgow-Edinburgh central belt and birds are often restricted to the margins of remaining large moorland patches, several of which continue to be managed for red grouse shooting.

Are heather moorlands good for mountain hares?

Mountain hares occur at some of their highest densities in Europe on the driven grouse moors of north-east Scotland, where benefits from habitat management and predator control appear to outweigh all but the most intensive culls[50]. Mountain hares eat heather and other moorland plants, so the managed burning carried out by gamekeepers to ensure a supply of young heather shoots for grouse is also likely to improve the food supply for mountain hares.

As foxes can account for up to 90% of mountain hare mortality[51], the predator control carried out on grouse moors may also help mountain hare survival. However, some evidence suggests that mountain hare numbers have been falling since 1999, and attributes this largely to shooting on grouse moors[52]. This is explored further in chapter 8.

© Tarquin Millington-Drake

3. Heather burning

Heather burning has a long history of use in managing moorland. It encourages the growth of new shoots, which are more palatable than older, woody heather to grazing livestock and grouse. Currently however, heather burning, especially over blanket bog stimulates an active debate about the possible effects on water quality, flood risk and carbon storage. These are complex issues, on which the science is not always available or clear, with a range of findings and interpretations. This chapter will discuss what is and is not known about heather burning and its place in our upland landscapes.

What is prescribed heather burning?

Prescribed heather burning refers to setting a fire on moorland that follows the methods laid out in law and codes of practice. The activity is also referred to as muirburn, rotational burning or managed burning. It is typified by planned burns of small patches of older heather (in some settings around 30m x 30m but sometimes larger), aiming for a low intensity, quick, 'cool burn' to remove the heather and grass canopy without damaging the underlying peat or soil layer[53–55].

Where is heather burning used?

Managed burning is widely used across the UK uplands as part of vegetation management for livestock and red grouse, as well as for conservation[24,56]. Concerns about its possible effects are greatest when prescribed heather burning is carried out over blanket bog (defined as peat more than 40cm deep in England and more than 50cm deep in Scotland) though its use on dry heathland can also provoke some concern. The issues discussed in this chapter refer mainly to the use of heather burning on blanket peat.

Why is it done?

As heather becomes older, it becomes less palatable and nutritious[57]. The process of burning small areas removes the older growth and allows the plants to regenerate afterwards[58]. New heather and grass shoots grow, and these provide food for red grouse, deer, mountain hares and livestock. Burning small areas of heather in different years leads to a patchwork, with heather and other vegetation of different ages and heights. This mosaic provides red grouse with areas that are suitable for feeding, breeding and cover[59,60]. Burning also suppresses tree and scrub spread and the eventual progression of moorland to woodland cover. Prescribed burning is also sometimes used to create firebreaks on moorland (see section 3.5).

When is heather burning carried out?

The law only allows burning to be carried out between October and mid-April in most of the UK (the end of March in Wales). Most burning occurs in the spring when the plant material has dried out, allowing it to burn, while cold, damp conditions underfoot mean the fire is most easily controlled. Burns are not performed in summer because birds and other animals are breeding, the daily temperatures are warm, and underlying peat may have become drier.

Are there guidelines or legislation that land managers must follow?

Yes. Westminster and the devolved Governments and countryside agencies set out and manage the rules for safe burning and can prosecute those who do not burn in line with them. For example, the Muirburn Code is produced for the Scottish Government by Scotland's Moorland Forum[61]. The Code provides good practice guidance for burning and cutting of vegetation, as well as statutory restrictions that must be followed. Land managers receiving public payments must also meet Good Agricultural and Environmental Condition (GAEC) requirements or face loss of financial support.

In areas which are designated as an SSSI, consent must be applied for in order to burn heather. Natural England does not as a rule allow prescribed burning on blanket bog habitats within designated areas; its position is that burning on blanket bog is generally considered to be harmful, but in exceptional circumstances it may be appropriate to carry out a one-off burn for the purposes of restoration. Where other habitat management options have already been explored, a consent for burning can be applied for as part of a blanket bog restoration project[62].

Are these guidelines followed?

Evidence looking at this is limited, but a case study on a moor managed for grouse shooting and sheep grazing in the Peak District showed that burning was within the widely accepted best practice guidelines. The authors of this paper do note that, while burning was found to be following the guidelines, the results apply only to that site and they "do not claim that the management of this moor is characteristic of UK moors in general"[63].

Is heather only burnt on grouse moors?

No. Although it is often used on grouse moors, heather burning is also carried out for livestock grazing on moorland, as well as other types of heathland. A recent study in Scotland looked at 26 estates and found that heather burning occurred on 23 of these, although grouse shooting was only the main land use on ten. The others stated their predominant management was for deer stalking, sheep grazing or conservation, with the specific conservation objectives set by the individual estates. Those estates that managed for grouse shooting had 15% of land managed by burning per year, compared to 5% of land on other estates[24].

Is there an alternative to heather burning?

Moorland vegetation can be maintained as a patchwork of heights and densities by burning, grazing and/or cutting. Grazing alone can sometimes be difficult to manipulate between too little and too much, but it is an important management technique used alongside burning or cutting. Cutting requires low slope angles and smooth terrain to avoid machinery damage or damage to the vegetation.

Where access is possible cutting may be a valuable tool in areas of high fire risk or fire impact, but care is needed to avoid compacting the ground with machinery. Where rainfall levels are high and there is little risk of tree and scrub encroachment, heather can spread naturally by a process called layering, where stems touch the ground, root and produce a canopy of younger shoots without intervention[64].

Why can grazing be difficult to control?

Livestock tend to congregate in certain areas on moorland, for example more sheltered areas in bad weather, or those where the available vegetation is more palatable. This means that these areas can become overgrazed, leaving other areas under-grazed. Grazing is best used for vegetation management when livestock is well shepherded, or fenced, into the areas which need to be grazed at that time.

3.1 Heather burning and biodiversity

What effect can heather burning have on moorland biodiversity?

A 2013 report by Natural England (NE) examined much of the scientific literature related to burning on peatlands, to which we refer heavily in this section[65], along with a comprehensive report to the Scientific Advisory Committee of Scottish Natural Heritage (SNH) published in 2015[66]. Most studies examined in the NE report indicated an overall increase in species richness or diversity when burning was considered at a whole moor level[65]. Because burning takes place in small areas leaving the majority unburnt in any given year, a mixture of habitats is produced which can support a wider variety of species[65].

An article examining moorland sites in Scotland over 44 years concluded that without burning, plant diversity decreased and stated "to maintain diversity, timely burning is recommended"[67]. However, as with any management technique, it is important that heather burning is done responsibly, according to best practice. The report to SNH noted that much of the conservation benefit from burning depends on local site management and conditions[66].

Can burning affect bird numbers?

As with any land management intervention, heather burning influences the habitat. Food quality, structure and composition are affected, therefore so are the number and diversity of species that live in the area. Some species are more abundant where there is burning compared to where there isn't[28]. Curlew have been shown to be more abundant as the percentage of recently burnt ground increases[24], though this effect isn't clear in all studies[68].

Golden plover prefer to nest in areas of short vegetation typical of sites where burning has recently occurred[69]. Benefits have also been shown for capercaillie where burning was used as a management tool in open pine stands with ground vegetation that includes bilberry, but is dominated by heather[56]. While some species seem to benefit from burning, those preferring longer, older heather, scrub or grassland may be disadvantaged, for example stonechat, whinchat, hen harrier, merlin and skylarks[28].

What would happen to the vegetation if the heather were not burnt?

It depends on the environment. Moors tend to be grouped together when discussing these complex issues, whereas in fact there are a range of different habitat types, including blanket bog/deep peat, and heather-dominated dry heathland[70]. For example, if heather was not managed on dry heathland, it would become old, degenerate and ultimately be lost. Scrub and tree regeneration would gradually occur, and would progress to a vegetation community of shrubs, bushes and trees[71].

Over blanket bog, this succession may be slower or not occur at all. Each moorland site is different, and vegetation responses depend on many factors, including altitude, rainfall, typical wind conditions, and grazing management. On sites where heather is flattened by heavy rain, wind, snow or gravity, natural layering may occur, which can allow other plant species to grow up through the opened heather canopy[64]. The amount of grazing on the moor will also play a significant role in how the habitat might change.

3.2 Heather burning and peat formation

What is blanket bog?

Areas that experience high rainfall and low temperatures, usually at high altitude on shallow gradients, with ground that is waterlogged for most of the year, can produce areas of blanket bog (sometimes known as blanket mire or blanket peat) where a significant peat layer covers the landscape[72]. Blanket bog has a particular mix of plants, usually found where the peat is saturated. In England, blanket bog is defined by a minimum peat depth of 40 cm; in Scotland this cut-off is 50 cm. Many of the concerns around the effects of heather burning focus on the impacts on blanket bog and its ability to store both water and carbon.

How is peat formed?

All vegetation can become peat in the right conditions, but certain plant species appear particularly good at forming peat. These include certain mosses and sedges which grow well in waterlogged conditions. The low oxygen content of the saturated soil on which these plants grow prevents their dead material from rapidly decomposing. Instead, the plant remains are slowly compressed as more dead material falls each season.

These layers of matter build up and eventually turn into peat. The peat is deepest where wet conditions are maintained (deeper areas of peat take thousands of years to form), and shallowest where the climate is drier and ground conditions more free-draining, factors which vary with relation to slope[72,73].

Does heather burning prevent peat formation?

No. Recent research has shown that peat formation can still continue when managed burning is used on moorland[20] and heather burning may be beneficial to some species that are considered peat-forming.

Three recent papers suggest that where the interval between prescribed burning is shorter (10 years), the extent of *Sphagnum* cover increases[74–76]. Ground under a 10-year burning rotation was found to have similar amounts of *Sphagnum* to areas that had not been burnt for 60 years, both of which had more *Sphagnum* than sites under a 20 year rotation[77].

One paper concludes that it found "no evidence to suggest that burning is deleterious to peat-forming species; indeed, it was found to favour them". However some studies indicate that the rate of peat accumulation may be slower where managed burning is used[20,78] and others have found burned areas had less *Sphagnum* and more heather[77], although the difference was small[79]. Any burning will cause damage to the vegetation, but it is the nature of that damage and the vegetation response to it which is important. Some evidence shows that where moorland is wetter, this can mitigate any damage caused to the moss and litter layer by prescribed burning[80,81]. The evidence is conflicting and further research is needed.

How can heather burning encourage Sphagnum?

Though burning can slow *Sphagnum* growth in the short term, fire removes the dense heather, grass or sedge canopy. As long as conditions are suitable, for example the ground being wet enough, *Sphagnum* can then thrive because of the increased light and reduced competition.

© Laurie Campbell

What is *Sphagnum*?

Sphagnum moss is an important plant species on moorland. It is a moss which is often associated with peat formation, thriving in wet conditions and is considered an indicator species for blanket bog in good condition.

Sphagnum mosses have cells whose purpose is to hold water. These are called "hyaline cells", and can act like a sponge, taking up and retaining water[82]. *Sphagnum* mosses do not decay in water, as many plants would, because they have special carbohydrate molecules in their cell walls, which make them more resistant to decomposition[83].

Sphagnum makes peat bogs more resilient to drought, with those topped with *Sphagnum* recovering better after dry periods[84]. Methane emissions are lower from *Sphagnum*-dominated peatlands than from other areas[85].

Why is peat burnt?

Burning peat is never the intention of moorland managers. Prescribed burning of moorland is sometimes mistakenly or deliberately called peat burning in the media. In controlled muirburn (which aims for a 'cool' burn) the plant canopy is burnt, with little impact on the ground layer and underlying peat. Peat maybe damaged by a 'hot burn', where conditions are more typical of unmanaged or wild fires. If the peat itself is burned, it can cause very severe damage and loss of carbon. The Scottish Fire Rescue Service (SFRS) is now actively promoting heather management, including the use of controlled burns to reduce the fuel load and prevent wildfires that can cause more damage[86].

What do you mean by 'cool' and 'hot' burns?

'Cool' burns pass quickly over the ground, burning the above-ground vegetation but having little impact on the humus or litter layer that sits on top of the peat, or on moss growing on the surface[54]. The temperature at ground level remains low and typically is barely raised below the soil surface. Achieving a cool burn requires knowledge and experience. Practitioners need to 'read' the ground conditions – how much burnable fuel there is, the wetness of the vegetation and ground layer, the wind speed and direction, slope angle, sun strength and air humidity to ensure that the burn passes over the vegetation quickly, has minimal impact on the ground layer, and can be contained within the area of habitat to be burnt.

'Hot' burns occur where the fire is slow moving, there is a large amount of fuel or the weather is hot and dry. These burns deliver more heat to a patch of ground for longer, affecting both growing plants and plant debris. This can result in damage to or ignition of the underlying peat, temperatures becoming higher still, and greater difficulty in controlling the fire. Such hot burns can result from managed burns being done in the wrong conditions or being mismanaged, or from wildfires breaking out.

3.3 Heather burning and carbon storage

Why is peat important for carbon storage?

Peatlands store around 30% of the world's soil carbon[20], with UK moorlands alone storing about 3,000 Megatonnes[87]. Thirteen percent of the world's blanket bog is found in the UK[88]. Introducing fire can affect the carbon dynamics of any system, so it is important to improve our knowledge of the effects on carbon storage when heather burning is carried out over blanket bog.

How does peat store carbon?

The growth of moorland plants takes carbon dioxide from the atmosphere and incorporates that carbon into the vegetation. When this vegetation dies, if the plant forms layers of peat instead of decomposing (the process of rotting would release much of the carbon again), this carbon is retained and stored within the peat[89].

Why is this important?

The amount of carbon that we release into the atmosphere is an important factor in global climate change. Carbon dioxide emissions, and how carbon can be captured from the air and locked away are increasingly important in our efforts to combat human-induced climate change.

Does heather burning release carbon?

All fires release carbon into the atmosphere. Each heather burn will release a small amount of carbon. However, reducing the available fuel load with the use of controlled fire also reduces the risk of wildfire, which carries the much greater chance of a large carbon release.

Does heather burning prevent carbon storage on moorland?

No. Recent research shows that carbon is still taken up and stored on moors on which managed burning is undertaken[90]. This paper supports others which have found that carbon uptake was slightly lower when comparing areas of no burning with areas that had been burned six times in the 60 years, but the difference was small[20,91].

What is the overall effect on carbon storage?

The "carbon budget" of moorland (the total amount of carbon taken up/released, giving an overall estimate of whether the area captures or releases carbon) and the effects of land management on this remain unclear. This is an area of active research. One study found that the carbon released as a result of prescribed heather burning over a cycle of 15-20 years accounted for less than 10% of the total carbon lost from the system over that time. Although carbon is released with heather burning, the authors concluded that careful burning management at that site did not have a major detrimental effect on the overall carbon budget for the moor[92].

This known limited loss of carbon associated with prescribed burning may reduce the risk of wildfire, which carries a much greater chance of huge carbon releases. However, another study also on blanket bog in the North Pennines found that areas managed with prescribed burning release less carbon overall than those which were unburnt[90]. This is a complex area of science and there are many other considerations, for example the role of producing charcoal through prescribed burning. Charcoal is harder to break down than peat or vegetation, which may mean it can have a positive effect on long-term carbon storage, but this remains a contentious area[93–96]. Research into carbon storage is ongoing.

3.4 Heather burning and water

Why is water quality important?

Upland areas provide around 70% of the UK's drinking water[97]. As well as all of us wanting to drink clean water, the EU has set standards for water quality that go beyond its purity and safety to include its colour. Water from peatlands is naturally discoloured as a result of draining through the peat, so water companies must treat water from peatlands to meet these standards.

The uplands are an important source of the UK's drinking water © Steve Jackson

How does heather burning affect water quality?

This is still being studied, with different pieces of evidence suggesting different effects. There is evidence that in England burning may be associated with increased water colour, with some sources equating this to an increase in dissolved organic carbon (DOC) in the water[65]. However, one study showed that DOC did not rise in response to burning, and the colour of water is not always a good indicator of DOC[98]. Another showed that DOC in the nearby lake fell following a wildfire[99]. The picture is not clear.

Does heather burning on grouse moors increase flooding?

Although there are relatively few studies available, the authors of a Natural England report could not find any evidence that burning increases flood risk, and state that: "No evidence was identified specifically relating to the effect of burning on watercourse flow or the risk of downstream flood events. If there are any effects, these are likely to be highly site specific"[65].

A recent study examining the effect of rotational burning on deep blanket peat sites drew several conclusions. These include that the lag time to peak runoff is increased on burnt sites for most rain conditions – meaning that the movement of water is slowed down across areas managed with burning – and that, for the heaviest 20% of storms, the lag time is the same but that the peak flow is higher from burnt compared to unburnt catchments[100].

Although this study is often cited, there are flaws in the experimental design which have led to the findings being questioned by other academics[79]. Once more, the evidence base regarding a possible impact of prescribed burning on flood risk is very limited and inconclusive, particularly when considered in the context of moorland drainage, the impact of which on flood risk is also very little studied.

Why is the impact of burning on water not yet fully understood?

Results differ depending on the length of time since burning, and the scale at which the studies are performed. Effects may be different at smaller, local scales, compared to the larger, catchment or landscape scales. The possible effect of burning on water quality and amount of run-off is also complicated by interactions with other upland management, such as woodland expansion and grazing. These interactions have been relatively little studied[66,101].

3.5 Heather burning and wildfires

What causes wildfires?

Evidence looking at the causes of vegetation fires is very limited. The Fire Service Incident Recording System does not include cause or source of ignition, unless an investigation is conducted which is very rare for vegetation fires. Therefore, the relationship between the use of prescribed fire and the frequency and extent of wildfires on moorland remains unclear. This is an area which needs more research. However, evidence does show that increased visitor numbers significantly increase wildfire risk in the Peak District National Park, with more fires starting at the weekend or on bank holidays, than on weekdays[102].

What are the differences between prescribed fire and wildfire?

Prescribed burning is carried out in winter or early spring, and aims to achieve a 'cool burn'. However, wildfires tend to occur in spring or summer and are mostly accidental or caused by arson. They may cover large areas and burn with far greater intensity and severity, sometimes consuming all the available fuel above ground (fuel-load), as well as significant amounts of underlying peat[87].

How does prescribed burning affect wildfire risk?

The evidence is mixed, with one study finding that heather burning can reduce wildfire risk in the Peak District, where grouse moor management is associated with a lower frequency of wildfire[103]. However, there is also evidence that sometimes prescribed burns are not adequately controlled and can lead to wildfires[66]. There is evidence across the world for the benefits of prescribed burning in reducing wildfire risk[104], but there are not enough studies specifically referring to the UK moorlands, and experts call for more research[105,106].

Prescribed burning can play an important role in wildfire management. By decreasing the accumulation of old, woody heather, which can build up to a large stock of potential fuel, it can reduce the likelihood and intensity of wildfire[65]. In this way, prescribed burning is used to create fire breaks, which hinder the spread of wildfire. Specifically, it may:

1. Reduce the risk of a fire starting, for example around areas with lots of public access.
2. Prevent a wildfire spreading, by breaking up extensive areas of high, dry vegetation.
3. Protect particular landscape features which may be damaged by wildfire, again by using controlled fire to create firebreaks around them.

The Scottish Fire and Rescue Service supports land management that reduces fuel load, such as burning, cutting or grazing. The growing fuel load in the countryside is an increasing concern for them, as any fire that does occur will have a ready source of fuel and will spread quickly and exhibit extreme fire behaviour[86].

What are the consequences of wildfires?
The impacts of wildfire are not always predictable. Severe (slow, hot and very large) wildfires can lead to huge carbon release, peat damage, reduced air quality and habitat destruction[107]. There can be a cost to the public purse with extensive and prolonged use of the fire and emergency rescue services in difficult to reach areas and a high demand on volunteer control efforts from local moorland managers. However, less severe wildfire can have little or no lasting impact on habitat, environment or wildlife[66]. Public policy suggests it is best to prevent fires with a combination of controlling fuel loads and a variety of social measures[108,109].

Is there a consensus amongst scientists regarding the role of fire for moorland management?

No. In a complex and controversial field, there are inevitably differences of opinion. There are many reasons for this, including the interplay of different factors, and the complexity and variety of habitats under consideration. A simple answer to questions about the effects of heather burning is rarely available, and a balanced review of the facts often reveals a more complex picture.

This was highlighted by a series of papers in 2016, the first of which was by 13 authors calling for informed, unbiased debate on the role of fire in moorland management[106]. This prompted two response papers, and then an answering paper from the original authors[110–112]. The scientific debate continues.

By reducing the potential fuel load, prescriptive burning can reduce the intensity of wildfire. © Tarquin Millington-Drake

4. Rewetting moorland

After the Second World War, Government incentives paid for widespread moorland drainage with the primary aim of improving the land for livestock. This is now thought to have been misguided because the environmental impacts were not appreciated at the time and because this drainage did not achieve its intended purpose. It is often incorrectly stated that moor owners drained the moors for grouse shooting and that this practice continues. In recent years many grouse moor owners have contributed to blocking up these drains, thereby rewetting the landscape.

Why were our moors drained?

Although some moorland drainage has been carried out for centuries, often to enable peat cutting for fuel, the extent and intensity of drainage increased from the 1950s to the 80s[113]. During this time, government subsidies were paid to landowners for digging drainage ditches (known in some places as 'grips')[114]. Drainage was intended to remove surface water and lower the water table on moorland primarily for agricultural purposes[66] - to improve grazing for livestock, as part of the post-war drive for "more food from our own resources". In the same era, large areas of British moorland were drained for commercial forestry[115]. Woodland planting on the hill and hill edge continues to affect upland landscapes, habitat and water (this is discussed in more detail in chapter 9).

Weren't moors drained to help grouse?

At the time it was thought there may be benefits to grouse, from improved food and cover to reduced disease transmission[114], but this was not the main reason.

Did drainage have a positive effect?

Drainage failed to increase the vegetation which sheep prefer. Gripping actually decreased the amount of heather cover and caused the spread of unpalatable grasses[114]. Nor was there any benefit to grouse: drainage did not obviously reduce disease transmission; grips are a danger to young grouse chicks, which can fall into them; and the ditches are obstacles for livestock and people. On lower moors, drainage removes pockets of wet deep peat which reduces the diversity of invertebrates, especially affecting those insects which emerge in spring and are a major component in the diet of young grouse[114]. As far back as 1970 when government grants for drainage were at their height, GWCT advised that draining on level waterlogged peat was slow, costly, usually ineffective, and could lead to gully erosion[116].

What are the effects on peat and carbon storage?

Due to its low density, peat is highly vulnerable to erosion, particularly through the action of running water over bare ground. By lowering the water table, drainage can cause the peat layer to shrink - leading to subsidence and increased erosion. This means that drains cut 50cm deep may erode down to several metres[105]. Healthy peat acts as a carbon store, locking in carbon, but drying peat out increases its rate of decomposition with the potential for it to release that carbon[117]. Drainage can also reduce the abundance of peat forming plants such as *Sphagnum* moss and cotton grass, which prefer wetter conditions[117].

What effects did moorland drainage have on water?

Upland drainage has been associated with several negative impacts on water. These include affecting the flow of water over and through the soil, increases in the rate at which water runs off the moor into rivers during rainstorms, otherwise known as flood peaks[115], greater sediment flow into river systems[105] and increased colouration of water from the peat[118]. Levels of dissolved organic carbon (DOC) in water running off the moor have shown to be significantly higher on drained slopes[119]. This leads to a significant cost for water companies, which are required to remove it in order to comply with water quality standards.

What is happening with moorland drains now?

Many upland landowners, including grouse moor owners, are actively blocking drains to restore moorland, both at their own expense and with support from Government agri-environment funding and other grants. The Moorland Association has reported an estimate by Natural England that around 18,000 hectares of moorland habitat on grouse moors has been restored in this way across northern England[120]. Similar schemes and activity are underway in Scotland.

How are moors being 'rewetted'?

Various methods are used on a site-by-site basis. Typically, drains are physically blocked at intervals along their length. Drains can be blocked with peat if they are small and on a flat area. This method is preferred by land managers and is the most cost effective[121]. Larger drains have been blocked with bales made of woody stems of heather, or with wooden or plastic dams. Some drains can also be 'reprofiled' where steep edges are flattened out, reducing flow rates and encouraging plant growth.

Will this have a positive effect on flood risk management, sediment and colouration?

There is good evidence that drain blocking is an effective way to reduce the amount of sediment reaching the stream and river network. Drains damned at intervals along their length have been shown to have low sediment levels[105]. Blocking has also been shown to reduce colouration by between 60 and 70% compared with a drained site making it a highly successful technique in this regard[119]. Both the National Ecosystem Assessment and Natural England review indicated that the opportunities for rewetting to reduce run-off were few, their effect uncertain, actually increasing the risk of flood in some cases, but that it may be beneficial if done sensitively[113,122].

Will this have a positive effect on peat and carbon storage?

We know that rewetting can enhance peatland by increasing cover of healthy bog vegetation, in particular peat-forming *Sphagnum*, but responses are variable and more long term studies are needed[123]. It has also been shown to be highly successful in reducing DOC loss[119].

Peat erosion can be reduced by grip blocking[121], and focussing efforts on sloping drains is more efficient as drains on flat ground are much less vulnerable to erosion[105]. These effects are likely to improve peat health, and therefore benefit carbon storage.

5. Disease control on grouse moors

Red grouse are wild game birds, but they are susceptible to population cycles where numbers peak and crash, which are often driven by disease. These cycles can make it difficult to achieve a consistent shootable surplus, which also means that income which helps offset some of the costs of managing for grouse shooting and wider public benefits on moorland is unpredictable. Veterinary medicine is used on grouse moors to reduce the impacts of some diseases and help stabilise grouse numbers.

This chapter will look at the two infections for which grouse are treated and the disease control measures applied. The first, strongylosis is caused by a parasitic thread worm which lives in the guts of grouse and can be controlled with an anthelmintic (worming) drug administered on quartz grit, which the grouse naturally eat to aid digestion.

The second is Louping-ill Virus, which is controlled by targeting the sheep ticks that can carry it. Louping-ill is also a threat to livestock (most often sheep) on moors also through external blood-sucking ticks. Finally, the chapter will look at the impact of the disease respiratory cryptosporidiosis on grouse, for which there is no effective treatment.

5.1 Strongylosis and medicated grit

What is strongylosis?
Strongylosis is caused by the strongyle worm *Trichostrongylus tenuis*. It infects the guts of red grouse, reducing gut efficiency, and therefore impacting the bird's condition, which can ultimately cause the death of the bird if worm burdens are high enough.

What effect do strongyle worms have?
We know from our research that high worm burdens can reduce both grouse breeding success[124] and adult survival, including making them more vulnerable to predation[125]. High levels of parasitic worms in some years can cause large numbers of grouse to die, leading to cyclical fluctuations with numbers crashing every 4-6 years[124].

Is this a recent issue?
No. The interest in avoiding cyclical crashes is not new. The issue has concerned grouse managers since the early 20th century. The 1911 Lovat research study into red grouse 'In Health and Disease' was largely driven by this problem[126].

In recent decades, the renewed stimulus to understand grouse population cycles came following a decline in grouse abundance in the 1970s. With this came the realisation that multiple factors - more predators, moors increasingly separated from each other by forestry and farmland, tick borne disease and climate change - were at risk of exacerbating the down-turns in grouse cycles so that they might prevent grouse recovery; with subsequent financial implications for the profitability of the shoot[127].

How was strongylosis first treated?

Trials conducted in the 1980s showed that catching hen grouse at night and treating them with an oral worming drug reduced worm burdens[127], and therefore allowed treated hens to produce and rear more young[128].

What effect did this have on grouse population crashes?

Treatment with worming drugs improved bird condition and survival, and this prevented grouse population crashes[129]. From this initial research "medicated" grit was first developed in the late 1980s[130].

What is medicated grit?

Red grouse consume naturally occurring grit to help break down and digest heather, their main food source. Grouse moor managers regularly put out boxes of quartz grit to facilitate this for grouse. Medicated grit is quartz grit coated with a thin layer of fat that is impregnated with a worming drug[130]. When it was first developed, the drug used was fenbendazole[6]. In 2007, an improved formulation of medicated grit was developed, using flubendazole, an alternative drug from the same family already licenced for use in game birds.

Is flubendazole safe?

Yes. It is a licenced human medicine and veterinary drug that is routinely given to livestock and game birds to treat different intestinal worms. Sheep are regularly treated with a different group of anthelmintics throughout the year against a range of gut parasites to prevent loss of condition and poor lambing.

Medicated grit is made available in trays, which can be closed as necessary to prevent or allow access as appropriate. © GWCT

Was the introduction of medicated grit effective?

Yes. The first experimental study looking at this showed that adult grouse from an area treated with medicated grit had significantly lower worm burdens than those from an untreated reference area. On the treated area, chick survival was significantly higher and hens reared more than twice as many chicks[130]. When treatment across the two areas was reversed, grouse on the second area then performed better, illustrating that the effect was down to the medication rather than other aspects of the study sites.

Do moor managers provide medicated grit all the time?

No. Veterinary drug use is regulated, and medicated grit is prescribed under licence by a vet. Vets should only prescribe medication when there is a demonstrable need for it. Demonstrating a need to use medicated grit involves an analysis of worm burden, either by counting the number of worms in adult grouse, or by counting the number of worm eggs in their droppings. The worm burden found at analysis will help determine a suitable course of action. In reality, grouse moor managers sometimes request, and vets sometimes provide, grit when it is unnecessary, and this inappropriate use escalates the likelihood of worms becoming resistant to the drug and the medication no longer working[131]. Targeted usage helps reduce the risk of resistance developing within the worm population[132], thus allowing the drug to remain effective.

How often is it likely to be needed?

A recently published GWCT study found that medicated grit usage varies markedly between moors. It may be needed every year on wetter blanket bog moors in the west, but may be only every 3-5 years on drier heath moors in the east[131]. Grit is provided in trays, which can be closed as necessary to prevent or allow access as appropriate. For example, the drug must be withdrawn a minimum of 28 days before grouse are shot to prevent drug residues entering the food chain.

Do we aim to remove all worms?

No. Current best practice advice on controlling parasites, based on management of livestock, is to leave 10% of the population untreated to help offset the build-up of resistance[133]. For more information about best practice for using medicated grit, see both GWCT guidance and best practice advice such as the Principles of Moorland Management (https://www.moorlandforum.org.uk/pomm-guidance-documents).

What effects could medicated grit be having on the environment or other species?

As a licensed medication, flubendazole has passed thorough investigations into the effect on non-target species, as well as the wider environment, and toxicity data are freely available[134]. However, it is important to continually review such possibilities and the GWCT have recently announced their funding of a three-year study with Leeds University to look at the degree of contamination of moorland soils and watercourses by flubendazole and their breakdown products.

5.2 Ticks and Louping-ill Virus

What are sheep ticks?
Sheep ticks *(Ixodes ricinus)* are spider-like blood-sucking parasites that feed on a wide range of host species. They have a four-stage lifecycle: egg, larvae, nymph and adult. They can transmit diseases such as Lyme disease (Borrelia) and Louping-ill virus (LIV) that can have an impact on livestock, wildlife and humans.

What is Louping-ill?
Louping-ill is a virus transmitted by sheep ticks which can cause fevers and neurological symptoms. It is often fatal in flocks of sheep which have no immunity to it. Ticks become infected with LIV when they feed on a host that has high levels of the virus already in its bloodstream. Previously, a vaccine was available for sheep, which helped prevent the spread of disease however this is no longer in production[135]. The main tick species that feeds on sheep or deer also feeds on red grouse, so ticks can pass LIV to grouse. LIV disease can cause around 80% mortality amongst grouse chicks in laboratory conditions[136], through effects on the nervous system causing loss of muscle control and lesions in the brain[137].

Do ticks present a threat to other moorland birds?
Ticks also feed on other moorland birds. Although we don't know whether waders such as curlew can become infected with LIV, high tick burdens can reduce body condition in their chicks, which may impact on survival[138,139]. In one study, chicks in 91% of curlew

broods carried ticks, with an average 4.5 ticks per chick, and a maximum of 64 ticks on one individual[139]. As well as feeding on red grouse chicks, ticks were also found on the chicks of all bird species sampled on one moor in North Wales. These were black grouse, curlew, meadow pipit and Canada goose[140].

Sheep ticks can transmit diseases such as Lyme disease and Louping-ill virus. © GWCT

Do ticks also affect humans?

Yes. Sheep ticks also bite humans. Under specific circumstances, humans can get LIV and it causes the same neurological problems[135], ticks are also a vector for the *Borrelia* parasite that causes Lyme disease, leading to flu like symptoms, joint pain and in extreme cases, paralysis. This can be very serious if not diagnosed and treated.

Are tick numbers changing?

Tick burden and abundance appear to have risen since the early 1980s. There is some evidence that climate change and changing numbers of deer have played its part in a steady increase in tick numbers since the 1980s. Two studies of the tick burden on red grouse chicks found that between 1985 and 2003, the proportion of grouse chicks per brood carrying ticks on the study sites rose from 4% to 92%. The average number of ticks per chick also rose in this period, from 2.6 to 12.7[141,142].

How can tick numbers be controlled on moorland?

Ticks are controlled by treating the sheep grazing on moorland, which can then kill the ticks that become attached to them. When used in this way, sheep are referred to as tick mops. Controlling the numbers of alternative wild hosts such as deer may also be beneficial, especially if combined with the use of sheep as tick mops.

How can treating sheep help reduce the tick burden in grouse?

For farming purposes, sheep are usually treated with anti-tick medication (acaricides) twice per summer. A GWCT paper from 2012 showed that increasing this to four treatments, either by dipping the sheep or using a pour-on medication, reduced tick burdens on grouse chicks by 90%[143]. In this study, sheep were also vaccinated against LIV, and the proportion of chicks testing positive for LIV fell throughout the study, in relation to how long the tick treatment programme had been in place on that moor[143].

The LIV vaccine is no longer available, leaving tick treatment as the only approach for sheep. A recent study also confirms that on sites where sheep were treated with acaricide more frequently, on average red grouse chicks had fewer ticks. When sheep were treated at six week intervals, an average of 1.7 ticks per chick was found, compared with an average 14.6 ticks per chick when sheep were treated at 10 week intervals[144]. Where sheep are the main large animal host for ticks, this approach can reduce tick numbers very effectively as ticks which bite the sheep are killed. However, ticks also feed on other animals and if these alternative hosts are present in large numbers, this can reduce the effectiveness of treating sheep alone.

What other animals can ticks feed on?

Ticks at different life stages can feed on a range of hosts including voles, hares, red grouse, sheep, and deer. At each life stage the tick needs a larger blood meal, which means that adult ticks generally feed on larger mammals such as hare or deer rather than grouse.

Mountain hares can be an important host for ticks at all stages of the life cycle and can be the main host for adult ticks if sheep in the area are effectively treated. If sheep are treated adequately, then tick numbers fall, and the number on hares also falls. In a trial area where mountain hare numbers were reduced, the number of ticks on grouse chicks also fell, as did the proportion testing positive for LIV[145]. However, there is a lack of scientific evidence as to whether mountain hare culling can increase red grouse densities[146]. One GWCT study found no evidence to suggest lower tick burdens on grouse chicks occur at sites with lower hare abundance, in fact higher hare abundance was found at sites with higher grouse brood sizes, and a higher proportion of hens with broods. Conditions which are good for grouse appear also to be good for hares without showing an increase in tick numbers[144]. More work is needed to understand this relationship.

Can controlling deer numbers reduce ticks on the moor?

Management of wild hosts through cull management strategies and deer fencing has been adopted on some estates. Whilst the significance of deer as tick hosts is recognised, the role of mountain hares in this disease system is still uncertain. One study showed that reducing deer density by culling, or excluding deer from an area of moorland or forestry with fencing resulted in dramatically fewer ticks[147]. A recent GWCT study also found that sites with higher deer densities had higher grouse tick burdens, and grouse breeding success was lower[144].

Ticks carrying LIV can infect grouse and other birds © GWCT

Can the grouse be treated?

Studies have looked at the effect of catching and treating grouse with acaricide, either using a slow-release wing tag, a pour-on treatment or a leg band[148–150]. Although tick numbers can be reduced and, in some studies, chick survival improved, the results were variable. One paper used computer modelling to predict the effectiveness of treating grouse. It predicted that acaricide treatment of grouse might be effective in controlling ticks and LIV, but only if deer are at low densities (fewer than 10 deer per square kilometre), or if deer were more numerous, higher numbers of grouse would need to be treated, and that treatment must be effective for 20 weeks of the summer season. Grouse treatment was predicted to have a much smaller effect on overall tick numbers than reducing deer density[151]. Reducing tick numbers overall seems to be more effective.

What is the recommended approach for tick management?

As a first step, the introduction of a comprehensive and thorough acaricide treatment regime for sheep flocks throughout the tick questing period (at least from the start of April to end of October). If deer are present, we recommend assessing densities and any subsequent need for a reduction in deer numbers. The GWCT recommends that efforts to reduce the impact of ticks on red grouse should focus on a combination of deer control and an effective tick management programme for sheep. Controlling mountain hares should never be assumed to be needed or to be the first management action undertaken. The GWCT and others are producing guidance for best practice on sheep tick control, which will be available on the in autumn 2019.

5.3 Cryptosporidiosis

What is cryptosporidiosis?

A disease caused by a single-celled parasitic organism from the *Cryptosporidium* group. There are 18 different species, with *Cryptosporidium baileyi* infecting birds.

It infects the sinuses of poultry, gamebirds and many other species of birds, causing swollen eyes and an excessive production of mucus; like a severe head cold. It is associated with high concentrations of birds, including captive birds in zoos and collections.

When was it first reported in red grouse?

Clinical symptoms of *Cryptosporidium* were first reported and subsequently diagnosed in wild red grouse in 2010[152].

Where did it come from?

Nobody knows. It is possible that it has always been present in red grouse. Since initial diagnosis in 2010, red grouse on 50% of managed grouse moors in northern England have shown signs of infection and over 80% of moors in the North Pennines[153]. To date, apart from a small number of infected birds in the Lammermuirs (south-east Scotland), outbreaks have only been reported from grouse in northern England.

How is it transmitted?

The spore phase (oocyst) of the cryptosporidium life cycle passes between birds. It is found in the droppings and mucus of infected birds, which then infects other birds. Higher densities of grouse may increase infection risk, for example congregating around communal grit trays or natural moorland drinking pools in dry weather. Generally, the highest infection rates have been associated with a period when grouse densities, especially of young grouse, have been at their highest.

How can this be controlled?

Good hygiene at grit boxes may be important to reduce infection rates. The oocyst can survive for long periods outside the body, but does require water to persist, so making sure grit boxes are well drained can help to reduce transmission[154].

How many red grouse show symptoms?

Our survey work has shown that on average about 5% of grouse on a moor may show typical symptoms of cryptosporidiosis at any one time[153]. This incidence is highest in grouse which have no immunity, and when the disease has just arrived at the moor. Juveniles are most at risk from infection.

Does infection reduce breeding success and adult survival?

Yes. Infected hens breed on average a week later than healthy birds and whilst they lay similar sized clutches of eggs and hatch a similar proportions of clutches, chick survival amongst infected hens is only about half that in healthy ones. A small proportion of adults have been shown to recover, but mortality rates are estimated to be twice those of uninfected birds on the same moor[153,155].

6. Upland predator control

Predation control is a key component of grouse moor management and plays an important part in the conservation benefits it brings. Although this sometimes causes controversy, the benefits to both red grouse and other species are well recognised. This chapter explains the methods used and the impacts of predator control on moorland.

What is meant by "legal predator control"?

Lethal control of certain common generalist predator species is
allowed under UK law, without individual licences. The methods
used are regulated by legislation and are also guided by best
practice codes.

Is predator control only done on grouse moors?

No. Gamekeepers are not alone in controlling predators; many
conservation bodies control them for the protection of wildlife.
Foxes and crows are also controlled to protect lambs and breeding
ewes. Predator control is an essential part of supporting rare species
such as the grey partridge in lowland areas[156].

What predator species are controlled?

The main species controlled on moorland are foxes, carrion
and hooded crows but also stoats, weasels, rats and feral cats.
The abundance of different predators varies between regions, so
the number controlled of each, and the effort directed towards
controlling different species will also vary according to which are
relevant in that area.

How are they controlled?

Predators are controlled using a variety of methods appropriate to
local conditions, typically shooting and various forms of trapping.
The aim is to achieve humane management of the predator species.
A new range of humane spring traps are being brought in for stoats,
weasels and rats and these are used in a variety of settings such as
in walls or over ditches. Cage traps of various designs (Larsen and
multi-catch) are typically used for corvids. Non-lethal restraining
snares are used for foxes. Shooting, often at night, is commonly
used for foxes. These are all regulated activities in the UK, with
training recommended in all regions and mandatory in some
parts of the UK. Where predation is controlled, it should be done

effectively, so that the prey species benefits. It must be carried out humanely and it must be selective, targeting the species in question and avoiding non-target species as effectively as possible. Best practice is continuously researched and revised by the GWCT.

Why is predator control necessary?

The modern world has created an environment where generalist predators (those that take many different kinds of prey) thrive - sometimes to the extent that they can harm the conservation status of other species. For example, a recent review of five wader species in western Europe (oystercatcher, lapwing, black-tailed godwit, curlew, and redshank) found that nest predation has increased by around 40% in the last four decades[157]. Although adult survival remains high for these species, chick survival and nest success have both declined, and breeding numbers are falling[158].

Why do we control some species for the benefit of others?

Many years of practice and GWCT research show that reducing the number of predators can improve the breeding success and abundance of prey species. Predator control is typically the lethal control of predators to achieve this goal. Game shoots use this to produce a sustainable harvest of game, and species living in the same habitat as the game often benefit from this reduced predation.

Are predator numbers permanently reduced?

Predator species which can be legally controlled in the UK are typically widespread and common, and there is no current concern for their conservation status. In most cases, the effect of predator control on their population is often local and easily reversed. Predation control is typically needed year on year, because as the species in question are generally abundant, those that are removed are usually replaced through breeding, or immigration from nearby areas. However, where predator control is widely practised across large regions, for example where there are adjacent grouse moors, predator numbers can be suppressed on a broader scale. We need to be mindful to ensure that the conservation status of predator species is not impaired.

Do predators really have such a large impact on prey populations?

In some circumstances, yes. Since the early 1980s, the GWCT has carried out many research projects looking at the effects of predation, publishing numerous scientific papers in this area. These clearly show that predation can depress numbers of game and other wildlife, especially when prey are scarce relative to predator numbers[156,159,160]. Both breeding success, and longer-term abundance can be lowered by predation. This reduced abundance is caused by losses of adults, eggs or young. A recent scientific review paper found good evidence that predation is having an effect on the populations of ground-nesting seabirds, waders and gamebirds[161].

Does reducing predators help those vulnerable species?

It can, where predator control is done to an effective level and habitat is suitable. As well as improving habitat and controlling diseases, much of the benefit of grouse moor management, particularly for grouse, waders, and probably mountain hares, comes from legal predator control. An experimental test of predator control showed that it allowed some ground-nesting birds (lapwing, golden plover, curlew, red grouse and meadow pipit) to breed on average three times more effectively than when predators were not controlled, with knock-on effects for breeding numbers in subsequent years[5].

In this experiment, the benefit to breeding curlew numbers was marked. In the absence of predator control, curlew numbers fell by 17% per year. When legal predator control was implemented, curlew numbers rose by 14% per year (after a lag period as the new chicks reached breeding age)[5]. We have calculated that the low breeding success seen on moors where predators were not controlled in this experiment could in theory lead to a 47% drop in curlew numbers of after 10 years, with an 81% reduction for both lapwing and golden plover[163].

This is currently being assessed through repeat surveys. Bird monitoring at Langholm Moor since 1992 has also shown that breeding success for red grouse and hen harriers was lower when predators were not controlled, with numbers declining during this period for these two species as well as for some breeding waders[23,36].

When keepering was restored, breeding success for these two species rose again[37], along with increased numbers of merlin[39], curlew, golden plover and snipe[6]. A review of the literature on the effects of predator removal on gamebirds and ground-nesting birds found that predator control can increase breeding numbers, hatching and fledging success, and can be an effective conservation strategy for enhancing bird populations[162].

7. Raptors on grouse moors: illegal killing

The illegal killing of several species of birds of prey (raptors), including golden eagle, peregrine and particularly hen harriers has repeatedly been shown to occur on grouse moors, especially those managed for driven shooting. The conflict is well researched but remains unresolved, and there are still gaps in understanding the social and ecological issues involved.

This chapter draws on the extensive body of research into hen harriers on grouse moors to explore the root of the problem and how we know it is happening. Importantly, it will discuss why and how grouse managers could and should accommodate raptors on grouse moors in the future alongside maintaining economic grouse shooting and its conservation benefits.

7.1 The conflict

Why is there a conflict between raptors and driven grouse shooting?

Hen harriers and some other larger raptors eat grouse and their chicks[164] and can reduce the number available to shoot. While the harrier's main prey species are voles and meadow pipits, grouse chicks are an important part of their diet at times, particularly during the breeding season when they are feeding their young[28,165,166].

Why has this led to illegal killing?

Predation by some raptors can reduce grouse numbers and prevent grouse population recovery. Many gamekeepers, grouse moor owners and managers believe that predation by birds of prey, particularly hen harriers, reduces grouse shooting bags (the number shot) to a point where the shoot cannot be sustained. This perception was confirmed by the Joint Raptor Study (JRS) at Langholm Moor[167] (see below). This means the loss of jobs and income both directly for keepers and in the wider community[168].

The JRS showed that in some situations, particularly when grouse numbers are low, a high number of raptors can depress grouse populations and then suppress their recovery enough that grouse shooting cannot continue[164,169]. In this study, hen harrier numbers rose steeply from two to 20 breeding females and grouse numbers in late summer fell to levels where driven shooting was no longer economically viable[36,164,167,170].

What is the history of this conflict?

Raptor killing took place throughout the 18th and 19th centuries. Combined with loss of lowland habitat, this led to the extinction of the hen harrier from mainland UK by the late 19th and early 20th centuries, leaving regular breeding only on the islands of Orkney and the Outer Hebrides[31,171,172]. There was a gradual recovery back into upland areas of the mainland from the 1930s and 40s onwards. Hen harriers received full legal protection in 1954 with the Protection of Birds Act. However, the recovery has plateaued in recent decades and there has been a non-significant decline in breeding numbers since 2010, particularly in areas of moorland and forestry[172,173].

Is there evidence that hen harriers are killed on grouse moors?

Yes, and the illegal killing of other birds of prey has also long been associated with grouse moors. Data from 25 years ago (1988-1995) showed that hen harriers had lower nesting success on grouse moors compared either to other areas of moorland, or to young forestry plantations across Scotland[31]. Recent evidence using data from satellite tagged hen harriers suggests that illegal killing is still widespread on British grouse moors[38].

In 1998 another study estimated how many hen harriers could in theory be supported by the available habitat in the UK. The paper gathered evidence from across the world, and predicted that if all suitable UK habitat were occupied, numbers could reach 1,660 nesting females[171]. At the time there were thought to be around 600-700 breeding females. Subsequent estimates of potential harrier numbers have been higher[34], but many assumptions behind these figures have been challenged.

Is all this habitat on grouse moors?

No. Potential hen harrier habitat in this study included heath/grass, open shrub heath, dense shrub heath or mire (or bog)[171].

Approximately half of English upland areas are thought to be managed as grouse moors[7], so there are also large areas of potentially suitable harrier habitat in the uplands that are not grouse moors.

Is 1,660 nesting harriers realistic?

The estimates in this paper don't account for other variables like the availability of prey, changes in vegetation, predation on harriers and harrier nests or the willingness of grouse moor managers to continue to produce these good conditions for harriers in the event they can no longer shoot grouse. We know that harriers and their nests are predated by foxes[36,174]. Some of the habitat may not actually have been, or may soon have become, unsuitable. For example, when commercial forestry plantations mature, they become unsuitable for nesting hen harriers[171]. However, the UK could accommodate a much larger number of harriers in the absence of illegal killing.

Would more harriers cause problems for grouse moors?

The study suggested that the estimated 1,660 harriers wouldn't have too large an impact on grouse moors but critically this was if they were evenly spread across the suitable habitat. However hen harriers often tend to roost and nest in a semi-colonial way so high densities can build up in particular areas[171]. The potential problems on grouse moors come from the uneven distribution of nesting harriers, rather than from the overall number of breeding pairs.

7.2 The Joint Raptor Study

What was the Joint Raptor Study?

The Joint Raptor Study (JRS) was a five-year project with joint partners including GWCT, the Centre for Ecology and Hydrology (CEH), the RSPB, Scottish Natural Heritage (SNH) and Buccleuch Estates. It studied raptor predation on grouse, to work out the likely effect this would have on grouse numbers and hence the sustainability of shooting. The main study area was on Langholm Moor, a driven grouse moor in south-west Scotland, with data from five other study moors in Scotland.

Why was it done? What were they trying to find out?

Until the JRS there was little scientific information to support or reject the firmly held belief of some groups that birds of prey could significantly reduce grouse numbers. The JRS therefore assessed the impact of raptors on the numbers and bags of grouse over a five-year period[167].

Which raptor species were studied?

The hen harrier and peregrine were of particular interest, as were their prey species. The diet of harriers is largely small mammals such as voles and songbirds like meadow pipits and skylark, whereas peregrine eat a variety of mainly larger birds including crows, pigeons and thrushes. Both predate red grouse, with harriers taking chicks and adults, while peregrine mostly hunt fully-grown birds[167].

What was done in the JRS?

Despite legal protection since 1954, it was recognised that illegal raptor killing was still on-going in the British uplands. During the JRS an agreement was made to ensure that all raptors were fully protected at Langholm. Active grouse moor management during the project included rotational strip burning of heather and lethal control of generalist predators permitted by law, notably foxes, crows, stoats, and weasels. Numbers of red grouse and breeding raptors were monitored each year. The researchers studied the breeding success and diet of hen harriers and peregrines, as well as grouse abundance, and mortality of both chicks and adults. The abundance of other harrier prey, meadow pipits and skylarks, together with field voles, was also recorded[167].

What did it find?

Hen harrier numbers rapidly increased from 2 to 20 pairs in five years[37,167,175], with their numbers initially following an increase in voles. Peregrines numbers also increased from three to five or six pairs. Predation by harriers and peregrines appeared to hold the grouse population at a low level, preventing it from recovering.

Why did harrier numbers rise so high?

If conditions are right, many hen harrier nests can be found in a small area[171]. The JRS habitat was a mixture of grass and heather areas, which is good for hen harriers[28,170]. These conditions are ideal for their main prey species and during the JRS there were years with high vole numbers[36]. Plenty of prey, together with no illegal killing and low levels of predation on the harriers' own nests thanks to legal predator control by gamekeepers, helped boost harrier numbers[36].

What did these raptors eat on Langholm Moor?

During the breeding season, meadow pipits were the most important prey species for hen harriers. Meadow pipits provided 45% of prey items, and grouse chicks made up 12%. For peregrines, pigeons made up 56% of summer prey items, and grouse 10%. Grouse also formed an important part of the diet for both hen harriers and peregrines in the winter, based on studies of pellets and prey remains. Seventy seven percent of hen harrier pellets and 85% of peregrine pellets showed evidence of grouse having been eaten. Many more grouse were killed by hen harriers than by peregrines. Most harrier predation was on chicks, and most peregrine predation on adults[167].

What impact of raptors on grouse was found by the JRS?

Until the start of the JRS, grouse numbers tended to show regular fluctuations in relation to the abundance of their parasitic worms, with peaks every six years or so (see chapter 5 on disease control). In the years before medicated grit was used to control these parasites, these 'cycles' were usual on most driven grouse moors. However, during the JRS, raptor predation removed on average 30% of the potential breeding stock of grouse each spring. In the summers of 1995 and 1996, predation by harriers accounted for more than a third of grouse chicks[167,169]. This was estimated to have reduced autumn grouse numbers by 50%, and numbers failed to recover from the low part of the cycle[167,175]. On two nearby moors, where grouse numbers had previously cycled in parallel with Langholm, but where harrier numbers had not increased, grouse peaked in 1996 as expected[175]. This indicated that at Langholm predation by raptors was keeping grouse numbers low, rather than parasites. Grouse numbers remained too low at Langholm to support driven grouse shooting, which stopped in 1997.

Would changes in habitat management have helped?

Almost half of the heather moor at Langholm had been converted to grass between 1948 and 1988, largely as a result of heavy grazing by sheep[170]. Hen harriers favour such a mixed landscape of grassy and heather areas[28], so it was thought possible that increasing heather cover and reducing grass may help alter the balance towards grouse. Over the course of the study reduced grazing and heather management increased heather cover[22], but there was no evidence that predation on adult grouse at Langholm was influenced by habitat. However, harriers were more likely to find grouse broods in areas of grass/heather mix compared to pure grass or pure heather stands[176].

What did we learn from the Joint Raptor Study?

Raptor predation can affect grouse numbers to the extent that driven grouse moors are not economically viable for sporting purposes, particularly when raptor numbers are high and grouse numbers are low[169]. Without illegal killing, hen harriers can thrive when moorland is managed for grouse.

Is this applicable to other moors?

When raptors are not illegally killed, their breeding numbers vary considerably between moors. They tend to be highest where meadow pipits and voles are most abundant, which is generally on moors with a mixture of grassy and heather areas[28,167]. Langholm is considered an average moor in terms of its heather cover and meadow pipit numbers. This being the case, in theory similar moors could host similar numbers of harriers, which could impact upon grouse[170] but much of our knowledge on the grouse/harrier conflict is still only based on data collected at Langholm.

Does illegal killing of raptors still happen on grouse moors?

Evidence suggests raptors are still being killed on grouse moors. Data from satellite tagged harriers collected up until 2016 showed that harriers are ten times more likely to die or disappear in areas which are managed for grouse[38]. Other evidence based on distribution, breeding performance and recovery of dead birds strongly suggests that illegal killing of an array of raptor species still occurs on some grouse moors[29,38,165].

Why only 'some' grouse moors?

We know attitudes are changing toward illegal killing (see chapter 2). However, the evidence shows that illegal killing does still happen in some places[38], and it is vital to address the conflict and end this practice.

What happened after the JRS?

Driven shooting stopped on Langholm in 1997, but a low level of keepering continued until 1999, when grouse moor management largely ceased and only the head keeper remained. The GWCT continued to monitor bird numbers annually, together with vole and fox indices, until the start of the Langholm Moor Demonstration Project in spring 2008, so we have continuous data for birds and voles on Langholm Moor since 1992.

What happened to the number of raptors?

Hen harrier numbers at Langholm fell from 20 in 1997 to between two and five pairs over the next five years. Hen harrier breeding success, which had averaged 2.5 chicks fledged per female per year with 80% of breeding attempts successful, fell to 1.2 chicks per female and 39% of breeding attempts successful when the moor became unkeepered (2000-2007) and foxes and crows were not controlled[37].

What happened to the number of grouse?

Grouse numbers also fell. Average spring counts between 1992 and 1999 when the moor was keepered had been 28 birds per km^2, which fell to 12 per km^2 in the period 2000-2007 when keepering had stopped. Post-breeding counts in July fell from an average 59 birds per km^2, to 14. Grouse breeding success also dropped, having been on average 1.7 chicks per adult from 1992 to 1999, but falling to an average of 0.9 for 2000-2007[37].

7.3 Hen Harrier Numbers

What are the most recent estimates of the UK hen harrier population?

The most recent survey of breeding hen harriers was carried out in 2016 and reported 575 territorial pairs in the UK. 460 of these (80%) were found in Scotland, with 46 in Northern Ireland, 35 in Wales, 30 in the Isle of Man and four in England[172].

Are these numbers changing?

Overall, the UK population has declined by 13% since 2010. This change is not statistically significant across the whole of the UK but on both grouse moors and in maturing conifer plantations in Scotland the number of harriers fell by around half between 2010 and

2016[172]. However, 2019 was a successful year for breeding harriers with fifteen nests in England and 47 chicks fledged. Eleven of these nests were on grouse moors[177]. Continued partnership working such as at Langholm, and the Scottish Heads up for Harriers project, may be beginning to help address the conflict in conjunction with new approaches such as brood management (see below).

Are the low numbers just because of illegal killing?

Illegal killing is thought to be the main factor limiting their recovery. However, harrier numbers can also be affected by the amount of suitable nesting habitat[178], the abundance of prey species such as the field vole[28,36,166,179], and predation[36]. Data on harrier and merlin from Langholm suggests that the loss of keepering can reduce breeding success of these largely ground-nesting raptors due to increased predation by foxes, which may lead to numbers in the area falling[39].

These findings are supported by similar trends found on two other Special Protection Areas in Scotland where keepering ceased[25]. Others have noted that predation by birds of prey, windfarms, the weather, and human recreational disturbance may also be affecting raptor numbers[34,35,180,181].

What sort of numbers can there be without causing a problem?

Based on our knowledge about grouse and hen harriers from the JRS, we can predict the effect of harriers on grouse populations[182]. At one nest per 4,000 ha (9,900 acres) it is predicted that hen harriers would reduce autumn grouse densities by less than 10%. Given the area of moorland in England managed for grouse, this density would result in approximately 70 pairs of hen harriers on grouse moors in England[182] and around 220 pairs on all heather moorland in Scotland. In 2016 there were estimated to be four pairs of harriers on heather moorland in England and 460 harrier pairs on heather moorland in Scotland[172].

Are there target numbers to aim for?

In 2011, the Joint Nature Conservation Committee (JNCC), which advises the Government on conservation, published a report outlining a "Conservation Framework for Hen Harriers in the UK". Within this report, the JNCC identified target numbers for the hen harrier to be considered in Favourable Conservation Status in the UK[34].

What is Favourable conservation status?

In order to achieve "Favourable" conservation status, the different influences which are acting on a species need to be in balance, so that it can survive and thrive. For example, when considering a particular species there are four aspects which are taken into account: their range, population size, the habitat (extent and condition) and their future prospects.

What does this mean for hen harriers?

The JNCC have calculated that, for hen harriers in the UK to be classified as favourable there should be:

  a. At least 44% of apparently suitable habitat occupied
  b. 2.12 pairs of hen harriers per 100 km^2 of suitable habitat
  c. A minimum of 1.2 young fledged per breeding attempt

The JNCC report estimated the amount of suitable habitat there is per country, so we can calculate the numbers of breeding pairs that could render each country favourable for hen harriers. Breeding success would also need to be high enough, but with variation between different areas these numbers do not tell the whole story. They give a minimum, rather than an ideal number of hen harriers in the UK but may be a useful guide to progress. Based on this simple approach, conservation status can be thought of as favourable for hen harriers in Scotland and Northern Ireland, but not England or Wales, or the UK as a whole.

	Total km² of suitable habitat	Favourable number of of hen harriers	National hen harrier survey data (2016)
Scotland	36,971	345	460
England	6,636	61	4
Wales	5,068	47	35
Northern Ireland	3,049	28	46

7.4 Easing the conflict

What can be done to unlock this conflict?

The conflict itself has been the subject of many research papers, looking for and exploring ways to resolve it[183–187]. The Langholm Moor Demonstration Project built on the findings from the JRS, running from 2008-2017 to investigate potential means of addressing the conflict.

Why was another study done at Langholm?

Having demonstrated that raptor predation could indeed put a grouse moor out of business, the Langholm Moor Demonstration Project (LMDP) investigated whether the grouse population could be recovered from these low numbers, to a level that would support commercial driven grouse shooting, in the presence of breeding raptors[188]. The GWCT worked again with its partners Buccleuch Estates, SNH, the RSPB and Natural England. The specific aims were to:

- Demonstrate how to resolve the conflict between moorland management for red grouse and raptors.
- Maintain the hen harrier population, for which Langholm Moor is recognised as a Special Protection Area.
- Improve and extend the heather moorland habitat, compared to its condition in 2002.
- Improve grouse production to a level at which driven grouse shooting becomes economically viable to support sustained moorland management.

What did the project do?

The project included several parallel approaches: habitat improvement, predator control, diversionary feeding of hen harriers and disease management[188], with the following components:

- Habitat improvement – heather burning, cutting, spraying and reseeding, bracken control and reduced sheep grazing to improve the condition of the heather moorland, and expand the area of the moor on which heather was dominant.
- Predator control – fox, corvid (except ravens) and mustelid (stoats and weasels) control.
- Diversionary feeding – alternative food was provided on posts near to hen harrier nests by up to half, in an attempt to reduce the number of grouse chicks taken by hen harriers providing for their own chicks. Day-old poultry chicks and rats were placed on a feeding post near the nest for up to 60 days after hatching of harrier chicks. There are practical considerations to this approach. The food has to be replenished daily and so the nests need to be accessible for the gamekeeper, but the technique can reduce the proportion of grouse fed to harrier chicks[189].
- Disease control – medicated grit was placed in trays and made freely available to grouse, which eat grit to help breakdown and digest heather. The grit contains the drug flubendazole which kills parasitic worms living in the grouse's intestines (see chapter 5).

The ten-year demonstration project was planned to run from 2008 to 2018, but land management ended in February 2016 when the board felt there was no likely prospect of achieving the grouse shooting objective.

What was found?

Findings have been published in a series of scientific papers, summaries of which are available on the LMDP website. The key findings were:

- Hen harrier numbers remained low, at one to three breeding females, from 2008 until 2014, when they increased to 12[37].
- Red grouse densities quickly rose from low levels, to be two to three times higher within three years of management resuming in 2008[37], but did not rise high enough to support economically sustainable driven grouse shooting.
- This was because the survival of grouse chicks and adults were both too low[190].
- Diversionary feeding reduced the number of grouse chicks that were taken by hen harriers, compared to what would have been expected[191]. However, diversionary feeding alongside grouse moor management did not increase grouse numbers sufficiently to allow sustainable driven shooting.
- Average yearly increases were found for three species of wader: curlew 10%, golden plover 16% and snipe 21%. However, lapwing numbers remained low[6].
- The extent of heather was improved. Total heather cover increased by 10%, and the area over which heather dominated the vegetation mix increased by 30%[22].
- There was a high number of breeding buzzards feeding on the study area (12-14 pairs), together with an estimated 47 non-breeders[192]. Buzzards are opportunistic feeders, using a variety of food sources, depending on what is available. Depending on the method used to study it, red grouse were estimated to make up 1-6% of prey items taken to buzzard chicks[193]. Although grouse are a minor component of buzzard diet in both summer and winter[194], the presence of many buzzards at Langholm meant that overall they may have been impacting upon the ability of grouse to recover, assuming that that all grouse eaten by buzzards were killed by buzzards and not merely scavenged[192].

A final report summarising the science and the partnership's findings will be published in 2019.

Day-old poultry chicks and rats were placed on a feeding post near hen harrier nests as part of the Langholm Project. © Laurie Campbell

How do we move forwards for hen harriers?

In 2016, the UK Government published its Joint Action Plan to increase the English hen harrier population[195]. It brought together several conservation approaches to try and safeguard the future of the hen harrier in England. It is a collaborative effort, supported by both conservation and field sports organisations, to protect both the hen harriers and the grouse moors.

What is the plan based on?

There are six elements to the plan, which are:

1. **Law enforcement,** prevention and intelligence: to reduce illegal killing
2. Ongoing **monitoring** of breeding sites and winter roost sites: to gather more information about the hen harriers we have and help with law enforcement

3. **Further research** into the movement of hen harriers using satellite tracking: to monitor hen harriers and their chicks
4. **Diversionary feeding** of hen harriers: to reduce predation on grouse chicks
5. Engagement study about their possible **reintroduction** across suitable habitat in England: to investigate whether moving hen harriers from a donor country such as France to suitable habitat in UK lowlands could be viable
6. **Brood management:** Trialling the temporary movement of hen harrier chicks to aviaries: where two nests are in close proximity, remove the chicks from the second nest, rear them in captivity and release them to suitable habitat further away.

7.5 Brood management

What is brood management?

Brood management is a form of wildlife management. If a hen harrier nest is established within 10km of another, the eggs or chicks from one of the nests can be collected and reared in captivity. When fledged, they will be released onto suitable moorland. If they are collected from a Special Protection Area (SPA) for harriers, they must be released back into this SPA.

Why will this help?

This is a trial of whether such management will allay the fear that many harriers will build up in a small area, and therefore remove the motivation to destroy them. An even distribution of harrier nests could allow for increased harrier numbers, with a lower impact on grouse numbers.

Why is brood management controversial?

Some people disagree with the principle of disturbing the nest and rearing chicks in captivity, even for release back to the wild. They feel that more criminal enforcement should be the main focus of harrier recovery, as numbers are very low in England a minimum population size should be established before brood management is instigated, and grouse shooting should be licenced or banned if illegal killing continues.

Others feel that all techniques should be tried to improve the outlook for hen harriers, and that this aspect of the plan could be the key that gives grouse moor owners and managers the confidence that their business or livelihood is not at risk.

Has this technique been used before?

Not for hen harriers, but it has been used successfully for the Montagu's harriers in Spain and France, to relocate them away from agricultural areas, where harvesting would otherwise destroy the nests[196-198].

What are the overall aims of the plan? What can we hope for?

It is hoped that the trial of the brood management scheme, as part of the Defra Hen Harrier Action Plan, will contribute to increased numbers of hen harriers in northern England. It is hoped that such novel non-lethal management techniques can change the social attitudes of those involved in upland land management to accept the presence of hen harriers on grouse moors.

It is also hoped that an improvement in the conservation status of hen harriers should help those who have sceptical views about grouse moors recognise that moors can and do deliver a net gain in biodiversity. The first hen harrier chicks to be brood managed were in 2019.

Langholm Moor Studies

Many years of research have been carried out on Langholm Moor in south-west Scotland, by joint partners including GWCT, CEH, RSPB, SNH and Buccleuch Estates. These projects looked into the relationships and interactions between birds of prey and red grouse. A series of scientific papers have been published based on the projects at Langholm.

There were three main phases of management:

- **1992-1999:** Grouse moor management around the Joint Raptor Study (1992-1996)
- **2000-2007:** Low level keepering, increased sheep grazing
- **2008-2016:** Grouse moor management with additional aspects such as diversionary feeding of hen harriers for the Langholm Moor Demonstration Project. Though the project was planned to run from 2008 to 2017, management ended in February 2016.

8. Mountain Hares

What are mountain hares?

Mountain hares are lagomorphs, a member of the rabbit family. They are sometimes known as the blue hare or white hare because of their blueish-grey coat in summer and white coat in winter. Mountain hares graze on vegetation such as heather, blaeberry and the bark of young trees and bushes, but they often eat grasses when they are available during the summer months.

Where are mountain hares found?

In Britain, mountain hares are widespread in the Scottish Highlands and Southern Uplands, and a small population occurs in the Peak District. Mountain hares are also present on some of the Scottish Islands where they were introduced (e.g. Mull, Skye, Hoy, Jura, Harris and Lewis).

What is the history of mountain hares in Britain?

Mountain hares are the only native lagomorph in Britain. They used to be found throughout the country, but when brown hares were introduced to England probably by the Romans, mountain hares became restricted to the upland regions.

Are mountain hares found on grouse moors?

Yes. Heather moorland that is managed for red grouse is a good habitat for mountain hares. This is probably because the predator control, combined with rotational burning that produces new heather growth, benefits both grouse and hares[199,200].

How many mountain hares are there in Britain?

The most recent population estimate is 135,000 mountain hares in Britain, with a wide possible range of between a minimum of 81,000 and a maximum of 526,000[201]. The range is large because until recently hares have been difficult to count accurately, and estimates are scaled up to cover more of the country that could not be surveyed.

How do you count mountain hares?

Several methods have been used to count mountain hares. These include walking transects during the day or night-time, counting droppings, mark-recapture by live-trapping hares, and using pointing dogs to flush hares during grouse counts. The James Hutton Institute and GWCT compared some of these methods and found that of those tested, night-time transects using a lamp were the most repeatable and cost-effective method[202].

Mountain hares are most active at night-time when their camouflage and "crouch and freeze" behaviour is likely to be less effective, so counting them becomes easier at night.

What other information do we have on mountain hare distribution and abundance?

Data from North-East Scotland were collected during red grouse counts using pointing dogs[50]. Long-term data from the GWCT's National Gamebag Census (NGC) gives us additional information on how many mountain hares are shot and on which estates[203]. Alongside these, data from the Breeding Bird Survey (BBS) collated by the British Trust for Ornithology (BTO) allows us to assess population trends since 1995 and species range[204]. In 2018, GWCT repeated distribution surveys from questionnaires that were previously carried out in 1995/6 and 2006/7.

The study has been the most extensive survey of mountain hare range to date and has allowed us to identify areas where their range has changed over the last 20 years. Early results indicate range contraction in South-West Scotland and on estates with no grouse shooting interest, compared to range increases in North-East Scotland on estates managed for grouse shooting. We expect these results to be submitted for publication in summer 2019.

What is happening to the mountain hare population?

Recent research on mountain hares in areas managed for grouse shooting has given conflicting results. In some studies, the national or regional trends appear to be relatively stable[50,203], while other studies suggest there is a decline[52,204].

There are four main data sources:

- National Gamebag Census – Data from hunting records in the UK since 1954 show population cycles roughly every 10 years, but no long-term trend in mountain hare indices from hunting bags since the 1960s[203,205].
- Hesford et al. (2019) – Count data gathered during red grouse surveys in the Scottish Highlands show that indicators of mountain hare abundance are up to 35 times higher and either relatively stable or increasing on driven grouse moors compared to moorland not managed for driven grouse shooting, where average declines were -40% per year in some areas[50].
- Massimino et al. (2018) and Watson and Wilson (2018) – Both studies reported declines in mountain hare abundance indices. Significant population declines in 34% of the mountain hare's British range occurred between 1995-2015[204]. A 30% decline in abundance was found each year between 1999-2017 on moorland managed for grouse in eastern Scotland[52]. However, an on-going analysis of GWCT hare data collected during grouse counts on the same estates surveyed by Watson and Wilson found no evidence to support these declines, and the analysis and conclusions used by Massimino have been challenged[206].

Why do mountain hare populations fluctuate?

Data from hunting records across Europe have shown that mountain hare numbers tend to fluctuate in cycles. The characteristics of these cycles vary, but typically the population can fluctuate from below half to almost double the average population size every 4-15 years[207]. Research suggests that mountain hare numbers can fluctuate naturally for many reasons including number of parasites, weather patterns, level of predation, presence of disease and habitat quality[208].

If numbers are so variable, how would we know if the whole population was declining?

Range contraction is often the first sign of a declining population. This means that the area in which the species lives is shrinking. In 2008 it was thought that the Scottish range of mountain hares was stable, but a more recent study of mountain hare distribution and abundance indicated significant declines within parts of their Scottish range[204]. Further surveys have been carried out by GWCT (with help from the Scottish Gamekeepers Association and Scottish Land & Estates), which covered more than 90% of Scotland and support the range contraction suggested by others, particularly within south-west Scotland.

A recent study shows that indications of mountain hare abundance are up to 35 times higher and either relatively stable or increasing on driven grouse moors compared to moorland not managed for driven grouse shooting © Ray Leinster

Which species predate mountain hares?

Mountain hares can be predated by foxes, stoats and weasels, and avian predators (birds of prey) such as golden eagles and buzzards[208]. Foxes are the most common predators of mountain hares, accounting for up 90% of hare predation[51].

What protection do mountain hares have?

The mountain hare is listed under Annex V of the EC Habitats Directive (92/43EEC) as a species "of community interest whose taking in the wild and exploitation may be subject to management measures". As well, Article 14 of the Directive requires member states to ensure that the exploitation of such species "is compatible with their being maintained at a favourable conservation status". This means that culling and recreation shooting of mountain hares is legal if it is proven to be sustainable[209]. In Scotland there is an open season from 1st August – 28th February. Mountain hares are shot for recreation, disease control amongst red grouse and sometimes to protect newly planted woodland[210].

Are mountain hares culled on grouse moors?

Yes. Mountain hares are culled on grouse moors for a variety of reasons including for sport as well as habitat and forestry protection. During the last 15-20 years, mountain hares have also been culled to help control Louping-ill virus (LIV), by reducing the transmission of the tick-borne virus to grouse chicks, which impacts their survival[145]. Tick control is now the most common reported reason for culling mountain hares[210.] There is more information on this in chapter 5. Until more work is done we have asked for a voluntary restraint on hare culling for disease control.

What happens to hare numbers when they are culled on grouse moors?

Mountain hares are most widespread in north-eastern Scotland, where there are large areas of managed grouse moors[210]. The number of hares found on these driven grouse moors can be up to 35 times higher than areas where grouse are not shot[50]. These facts, combined with evidence of increasing or stable mountain hare numbers on driven grouse moors, suggest that the possible benefits of grouse moor management (fewer hares being taken by predators and better quality food following heather burning) may outweigh the impact of culling that is limited in time and in area[50].

What impact would a ban on driven grouse shooting have on mountain hares?

This would depend on what land use replaced grouse shooting. Alternatives such as commercial forestry or possibly more intensive grazing may result in lower numbers. Research by GWCT reported lower abundance indices and declines in areas where moorland habitats have become fragmented through afforestation, which has created upland landscapes less suitable for mountain hares[50].

Similarly, research by the Centre for Ecology and Hydrology and RSPB reported declines in mountain hare abundance indices associated with conifer planting[52]. Others have suggested that the loss of grouse moor management to sheep grazing may contribute to mountain hare declines[211]. However, in areas which are designated, for example as an SSSI or SPA, commercial forestry is unlikely to replace driven shooting. Some alternative uses, including natural forest regeneration would provide habitat for mountain hares but at lower densities than are currently seen and thus potentially with greater risk of local extinction, if the habitat were fragmented or predation increased. Whether or not practices such as predator control or hare culls continued would also have an impact on hare numbers in future, if driven shooting stopped. It is important to remember that much of the mountain hare's habitat is at higher altitudes than managed grouse moors. In these higher areas, reported declines are less severe[52].

9. Alternative Moorland Uses

Moorlands are cultural landscapes extending back thousands of years and it is our management that creates and maintains them as moors. Like most land in the UK, management activity is driven by individuals or groups who own and use it for social and economic purposes. In the uplands, game management, livestock grazing, forestry and renewable energy generation support unique landscapes, habitats and wildlife to a greater or lesser extent. This chapter considers these land uses and their various merits.

What are the economically viable uses for moorland?

Historically, moorland has been less productive than other land and most grouse moors sit on land classified as Less Favoured Areas (LFAs), where agricultural production is more difficult. Its use is mainly limited to livestock grazing, commercial forestry, game management and renewable energy generation. Though able to provide some income, none of these activities are sustainable without substantial public or private subsidy. Commercial or state support is also needed for other uses such as nature reserves, carbon storage, or water management. The tourism sector benefits from these open upland landscapes but makes little or no direct contribution to their maintenance costs, with most tourism income going into local businesses[212].

Why is a mix of land uses best?

All land use has an impact on the environment and the consequences of the various economic models for moorland management will be discussed in more detail below. Different species thrive in different environments and our internationally recognised upland habitats are best supported with a mix of management across the landscape, including grouse moors[24].

It is important to understand that the known benefits, including internationally important habitats and species, would probably be lost if grouse shooting ended. At the same time, it is also important that moorland and heathland management is sufficiently flexible to adapt to changing conditions.

9.1 Alternative moorland use: Forestry

How much of Britain has been forested?

Commercial forestry blocks typically consist of fast-growing, often non-native coniferous species. Extensive upland planting started in the UK after the first world war and rapidly accelerated after the second world war, largely in response to government initiatives. UK forest cover has more than doubled over the last 100 years[213]. By 2019, 18% of Scotland was wooded and the Government plans to increase this to 21% by 2032[214,215]. Forestry has been one of the main causes of moorland habitat loss, with around 20% of former UK moorland now afforested with coniferous plantations[105].

Commercial forestry blocks have negative impacts on breeding curlew because of habitat replacement and increased predation. © GWCT

What effect does forestry have moorland habitats and wildlife?

Afforestation causes an ecological transformation, in which open ground habitats and their wildlife largely disappear and are replaced by a woodland ecosystem. Afforestation of the Southern Cheviots in southern Scotland is a good example of the impact of forestry on moorland birds. After 15 years, the forest canopy closed, and many species disappeared. The losses for that area were estimated to be

1,750 pairs of curlew, 1,200 pairs of golden plover, 200 pairs of dunlin, 25 pairs of merlin, and all the red grouse, snipe, redshank, wheatears, ring ouzels and hen harriers[216]. Declines in the numbers of ravens have been reported[217] and a review documents the loss of at least 5,000 breeding pairs of curlew from south-west Scotland largely because of forestry[216].

GWCT research into impacts of land use change in south-west Scotland also indicate that large-scale changes in land-use, including afforestation, more intensive farming and reductions in grouse moor management, are responsible for declines in several bird species, including oystercatcher, golden plover, lapwing and curlew[25]. One study of a 700km^2 area in Scotland suggested that afforestation accounted for 58-78% of the decline in black grouse numbers in the region[218].

Changes in grazing patterns of deer, voles and rabbits because of afforestation can affect the suitability of moorland near forestry for birds, by changing vegetation density, reducing invertebrate food for chicks[47] and potentially increasing the tick burden[142].

What are the effects of forestry on predation in the surrounding areas?

Both mammal and bird predators benefit from the cover of forestry blocks but do not restrict their hunting to within the forestry[219]. Bird communities in the surrounding moorland can be affected up to a kilometre from the forest edge, with reductions in golden plover and dunlin numbers, and reduced curlew breeding success[105].

Can upland forestry benefit some bird species?

There are 68 bird species breeding regularly in Scottish woodlands though they are not all found in every woodland[220]. The mix of bird species is largely dependent on which trees are dominant and bird densities are lower in uniform woodland. The age of the plantation is also important. The early stages of tree growth can create suitable habitat for black grouse and hen harriers, but when the trees grow and the canopy closes over the environment becomes unsuitable[221].

Are there other environmental effects?

Beyond impacts on biodiversity the most important effect of forestry is on soils and water. Before trees are planted, drains are often dug and fertiliser applied, which affects the nutrient composition of the soil and increases the release of carbon. Drainage lowers the water table, causing peat to shrink as it dries out (see chapter 4). This process accelerates once the tree canopy closes and can lead to large-scale cracking of the peat[105], which can occur some distance away from the forestry block itself.

Are there effects on water quality and flow?

Yes. There can be negative effects on the water quality and the amount and timing of run-off[105]. Streams that drain afforested areas tend to be more acidic and have higher levels of nitrogen[222]. Water flow is also affected, with total peak flow increasing initially where land has been drained then reducing once the trees mature, after perhaps 20 years[105].

Does forestry store more carbon?

The effect on overall carbon uptake and release when moorland is converted to forestry is not clear. There is an initial release of carbon during preparation and planting because of peat drainage and disturbance, but when the trees are growing rapidly in the early stages, they take up carbon. During this period forestry may absorb and store carbon faster than moorland. However, mature forests have low carbon uptake and after a period of several decades the carbon balance is thought to be fairly even between moorland and forestry.

There are many uncertainties in carbon budgets, which typically do not take into account the carbon that is found in streams draining moorland or young forestry or rates of erosion from forest drainage[223.] A review found that not all modified peatlands are carbon or greenhouse gas sources, just as not all "pristine" peatlands are net sinks. Equally, peatland restoration may not necessarily lead to a peatland being able to absorb carbon or greenhouse gas[223].

What happened when trees were planted in the Flow Country?

This large, rolling expanse of peatland in the North of Scotland is dotted with bog pools and is an important habitat for wildlife, as well as climate change mitigation. Successive government policies to plant trees and cut drains, mostly in the 1980s, resulted in 17% of this area being covered by coniferous forest[224]. This dried out the peat, changing the habitat and reducing its value for birds and other wildlife. The trees are now being removed.

What about natural regeneration, wilding or rewilding?

These terms are often synonymous with scrub or woodland expansion onto moorland. Wilding usually requires the decision to reduce or stop grazing and/or heather burning. As well as losing grazing on the area itself, this could cause neighbouring land to be more intensively grazed as well as increasing the risk of wildfire from increased fuel load (see chapter 3 for more information on wildlfires). There is as yet little evidence for the effect of wilding/rewilding on wildlife, carbon storage, effects on water or other important consideration, which must be provided if such a change is to be made on a large scale.

9.2 Alternative moorland use: Renewable energy

What kinds of renewable energy can be generated in the uplands?

By 2015 there were over 200 windfarm developments underway in Scotland, making onshore wind power the main source of renewable energy[66]. By 2017, renewable power output made up over 70% of Scotland's electricity consumption[225]. There are also small-scale hydro schemes which, though usually less visually intrusive, can have impacts on the ground.

What effects can wind farms have?

They can affect habitat, soil and the wider landscape. The main impacts on moorland habitats are from the loss of land for tracks, crane hard standings, turbine bases, control buildings, borrow pits and changes in drainage. Additional impacts can arise through the improved access provided by these developments, enabling recreational activities in areas which were previously inaccessible[66]. One study found the density of some moorland bird species near wind farms was reduced by between 15% and 48%[181]. Another found that the impact on moorland birds may be higher during the construction than the operation phase of wind farms, with lower numbers of red grouse and curlew during construction[226].

Are all the impacts negative?

Where forested areas are felled to return an area to moorland (albeit with turbines) over time this could be beneficial in enhancing overall biodiversity[66]. One study suggests some species such as skylark and stonechat may benefit from the habitat change during construction[226]. Where income from the windfarm is reinvested in surrounding moorland the increased management and small-scale scrub planting could benefit some species. Furthermore, providing renewable energy is a main priority for the country with clear benefits that must be weighed up.

9.3 Alternative moorland use: Farming

How important is farming in the uplands?

The UK National Ecosystem Assessment says that livestock farming over many generations has contributed to the cultural and environmental heritage of today's countryside, and many things our society values beyond food may depend on upland farming in the future. About 15% of the UK land area is upland farming[122]. Eight-five percent of agricultural land in Scotland is classified as LFA[227] and this is predominantly in the uplands. Sheep grazing has determined the appearance and habitat composition of UK uplands more than any other land use[66].

Sheep grazing has determined the appearance and habitat composition of UK uplands more than any other land use. © David Mason

How does livestock grazing affect moorland?

Comprehensive reports show that light, seasonal grazing by sheep is good for heather moorland and consequently for grouse[5,17]. However, European Common Agricultural Policy (CAP) subsidies for livestock farming based upon livestock numbers resulted in a 30% increase in sheep on UK moorlands between the 1970s and 1990s[223]. These large increases too often led to overgrazing on moorland. In recent years, with farming support moving from livestock number to area-based payments, grazing pressure has considerably reduced, and this can improve heather cover and condition. Observation suggests that heather regeneration following restocking has been considerable, but there is as yet little evidence for large-scale habitat improvements in response to this[101].

What sort of detrimental effects can overgrazing have?

Studies suggest that in England loss of heather moorland has mostly been due to overgrazing[228] whereas in Scotland moorland has been lost because of grazing and forestry[18]. The most well-established effect is the reduced condition or extent of heather cover, and replacement with grass-dominated vegetation[101,105]. Species that require a diverse moorland habitat and those that have a strong link to heather for food and cover, such as red grouse, hen harrier, merlin, mountain hare and red deer, tend to decline in abundance and productivity with these changes. However, other species such as skylark and meadow pipit, may benefit from a change to grassland provided this is not too heavily grazed[28].

Are there any other impacts?

Studies have found that overgrazing can cause soil erosion and may increase flood risk. A review from 2007 suggested that grazing may impact water flow across moorland to the extent that stopping grazing may reduce flood risk[105]. Its effect on carbon capture and storage is variable and there is little impact on water quality[66,101].

Does all grazing cause these problems?

A light, preferably mixed grazing regime seems to provide benefits in terms of environmental services and biodiversity. However, such a regime is not economically viable without extra funding, so is often supported by private investment in the form of grouse management or public subsidy through agri-environment grants[101]. The management techniques that are employed to improve grazing, such as drainage (see chapter 4) and liming, can be damaging to the heather moorland and its ecosystem[53].

Can there be a balance?

Grouse moors need sheep grazing to provide habitat and, in some places, to help control tick numbers. Sheep graziers need moorlands to summer graze their flock, preserving their improved grass for winter, and they can benefit from nearby gamekeeping which reduces the impacts of foxes and crows. Management arrangements between grouse moors and sheep graziers provide an incentive to manage heather moorland sustainably, maximising positive outcomes such as high nature value and rural employment, while minimising habitat damage. Heather moorland is important both as an EU priority habitat and as a globally rare habitat. With much of our moorland protected by designations like Sites of Special Scientific Interest, Special Areas of Conservation or Special Protection Areas, owners will have both their own commitments to upland investment, as well as public requirements to consider. Moorland is often considered a 'Less Favoured Area' (LFA) for farming, being challenging for agricultural production or forestry because of natural constraints or conservation considerations, but it can be of high value for nature. These restrictions mean that land management options are limited, but driven grouse shooting can provide a means to generate income, which can recover the costs of managing and maintaining the moorland and its wildlife.

10. Economics of grouse moors

What is the economic value of grouse shooting?

A recent report indicated that grouse moor owners in England spend £52.5 million every year on moorland management[168]. The report also indicated that businesses associated with grouse shooting benefit by some £15.2 million every year. These include game dealers, accommodation providers, equipment suppliers, catering establishments and transport operators, often based in remote rural locations who depend on grouse shooting as the main economic driver outside the tourist season. Grouse moors in England support 1,520 Full Time Equivalent (FTE) jobs. Seven hundred are directly involved with grouse moor management and a further 820 jobs in related services and industries.

Grouse moors in Scotland and England support the equivalent of over 4,000 full time jobs © Steve Jackson

In Scotland, it was found that there were around 2,500 FTE jobs (both direct and indirect) reliant on the grouse moor sector in 2009 with £14.5 million spent on wages related to grouse moor management and support activities, and a total 'Gross Value Added' contribution of £23 million to the Scottish economy. The Scottish Moorland Group reported an average annual wage bill of £210,000 for estates involved in grouse moor management[188,229].

What costs are involved in managing moorland for conservation and driven grouse shooting?

Some of the main costs are heather management or restoration (such as muirburn, cutting or re-seeding), bracken control, livestock management, predator and deer control, track maintenance, salaries, housing and equipment (e.g. tractors, ATVs).

Can driven grouse shooting cover these costs?

The income from driven grouse shooting can make a valuable contribution to the costs of running both moorland and shoot management. If there are enough grouse, then it is possible to cover the costs in a shooting season.

Can these costs be consistently met?

No, not always. Even though some of the variability in red grouse numbers from year to year can now be smoothed out using the available management tools such as medicated grit, it is impossible to eliminate the risks. For instance, extreme weather can impact on grouse numbers especially if combined with parasite problems, grouse are an arctic species and relatively well adapted to cold and wet weather. Where the numbers of grouse drop to levels at which further shooting may risk reducing the desired level of breeding stock for the next year, owners may decide to run a restricted shoot programme, or they might decide to cancel all shooting. So, the income can still vary from year to year, making it difficult to cover the costs of heather habitat and grouse management on a regular basis.

What else can affect the chances of covering management costs?

Owners and managers need to ensure that their stock of grouse is sufficient to absorb not only the effect of predators that can be legally controlled, (such as foxes and crows), but also the impact from protected species, particularly raptors. GWCT's involvement in projects like the Langholm Moor Demonstration Project and the

Hen Harrier Brood Management Scheme is about finding a science-based answer to the conflict between raptors and management for red grouse (see chapter 7).

The income from driven grouse shooting helps to support the cost of moorland management © Tarquin Millington-Drake

Could walked-up shooting replace driven shooting?

Allowing higher density (driven) grouse moors to decline to lower density (walked-up) ones would result in greater loss of income than the corresponding saving, and would not be economically viable[7], as well as not bringing the same level of conservation benefits.

What might happen if we can't find a way that allows moor owners a reasonable chance to recover costs on moorland management?

If moor owners aren't given the scope to recover some of the costs of moorland management through driven grouse shooting, this could result in abandonment of grouse management and gamekeepers losing their employment. Losing gamekeepers from the uplands would jeopardize the protection of heather moorland and Special Protection Areas for birds, large areas of which are keepered and which also support high numbers of breeding waders like curlews[7]. If made the responsibility of the public sector, protection of the heather moorland habitat and the conservation benefits that brings would require huge amounts of public funding[19].

11. References

1   Musgrove, A., Aebischer, N.J., Eaton, M., Hearn, R., Newson, S., Noble, D., Parsons, M., Risely, K. & Stroud, D. (2013). Population estimates of birds in Great Britain and the United Kingdom. *British Birds*, **106**:64–100.

2   Eaton, M., Aebischer, N.J., Brown, A., Hearn, R., Lock, L., Musgrove, A., Noble, D., Stroud, D. & Gregory, R. (2015). Birds of conservation concern 4: the population status of birds in the UK, Channel Islands and Isle of Man. *British Birds*, **108**:708–746.

3   Tharme, A.P., Green, R.E., Baines, D., Bainbridge, I.P. & O'Brien, M. (2001). The effect of management for red grouse shooting on the population density of breeding birds on heather-dominated moorland. *Journal of Applied Ecology*, **38**:439–457.

4   Thompson, D.B.A., Gillings, S.D., Galbraith, C.A., Redpath, S.M. & Drewitt, J. (1997). The contribution of game management to biodiversity: a review of the importance of grouse moors for upland birds. In: *Biodiversity in Scotland: Status, Trends and Initiatives*: 198–212. (eds. Fleming, L.V., Newton, A.C., Vickery, J.A. & Usher, M.B.) TSO. Edinburgh.

5   Fletcher, K., Aebischer, N.J., Baines, D., Foster, R. & Hoodless, A.N. (2010). Changes in breeding success and abundance of ground-nesting moorland birds in relation to the experimental deployment of legal predator control. *Journal of Applied Ecology*, **47**:263–272.

6   Ludwig, S.C., Roos, S. & Baines, D. (2019). Responses of breeding waders to restoration of grouse management on a moor in South-West Scotland. *Journal of Ornithology*, doi:10.1007/s10336-019-01667-6

7   Sotherton, N.W., Tapper, S.C. & Smith, A. (2009). Hen harriers and red grouse: economic aspects of red grouse shooting and the implications for moorland conservation. *Journal of Applied Ecology*, **46**:955–960.

8   UK Government, D. (2016). Ban driven grouse shooting: Government response. Available at: https://petition.parliament.uk/petitions/104441?reveal_response=yes#response-threshold.

9   Newman, C. (2017). *Whose moors are they? National Geographic*: May.

10   Cunningham, R. (2017). Meeting of the Scottish Parliament: Wildlife Crime.

11   Tallis, J., Meade, R. & Hulme, P. (1998). Blanket mire degradation. In: *British Ecological Society*: 1–2. (eds. Tallis, J., Meade, R. & Hulme, P.) Manchester.

12   United Nations Environment Programme. (1992). Rio Declaration on Environment and Development. *The United Nations Conference on Environment and Development*: Available at: http://www.unep.org/documents.multilingual/default.asp?documentid=78&articleid=1163.

13   Thompson, D.B., MacDonald, A.J., Marsden, J.H. & Galbraith, C. (1995). Upland heather moorland in Great Britain: a review of international importance, vegetation change and some objectives for nature conservation. *Biological Conservation*, **71**:163–178.

14   Backshall, J. (2001). Chapter 6: Moorland. In: *The upland management handbook (SC26)*: Natural England.

15   Bumblebee Conservation Trust. GWCT. (2017). *Managing moorland... for bumblebees. Land management series. Factsheet 10:* Available at: https://www.bumblebeeconservation.org/wp-content/uploads/2017/08/BBCT_Land_Factsheet_10_Moorland_management.pdf.

16   Haysom, K.A. & Coulson, J.C. (1998). The *Lepidoptera* fauna associated
      with *Calluna vulgaris*: effects of plant architecture on abundance and
      diversity. *Ecological Entomology*, **23**:377–385.

17   Sim, I.M.W., Gregory, R.D., Hancock, M.H. & Brown, A.F. (2005).
      Recent changes in the abundance of British upland breeding birds. *Bird
      Study*, **52**:261–275.

18   Robertson, P.A., Park, K. & Barton, A. (2001). Loss of heather moorland
      in the Scottish uplands: the role of red grouse management. *Wildlife
      Biology*, **7**:37–42.

19   Sotherton, N.W., May, R., Ewald, J.A., Fletcher, K.L. & Newborn,
      D. (2009). Managing uplands for game and sporting interests. An
      industry perspective. In: *Drivers of Environmental Change in Uplands*:
      241–260. (eds. Bonn, A., Allott, T., Hubacek, K. & Stewart, J.) Routledge.
      Abingdon.

20   Marrs, R.H., Marsland, E.L., Lingard, R., Appleby, P.G., Piliposyan,
      G.T., Rose, R.J., O'Reilly, J., Milligan, G., Allen, K.A., Alday, J.G.,
      Santana, V., Lee, H., Halsall, K. & Chiverrell, R.C. (2019). Experimental
      evidence for sustained carbon sequestration in fire-managed, peat
      moorlands. *Nature Geoscience*, **12**:108–112.

21   Ward, S.E., Ostle, N.J., Oakley, S., Quirk, H., Henrys, P.A. & Bardgett,
      R.D. (2013). Warming effects on greenhouse gas fluxes in peatlands are
      modulated by vegetation composition. *Ecology Letters*, **16**:1285–1293.

22   Ludwig, S.C., Aebischer, N.J., Bubb, D., Richardson, M., Roos, S.,
      Wilson, J.D. & Baines, D. (2018). Population responses of red grouse
      Lagopus lagopus scotica to expansion of heather *Calluna vulgaris* cover on a
      Scottish grouse moor. *Avian Conservation and Ecology*, **13**:1–12.

23   Baines, D., Redpath, S., Richardson, M. & Thirgood, S. (2008). The
      direct and indirect effects of predation by Hen Harriers *Circus cyaneus* on
      trends in breeding birds on a Scottish grouse moor. *Ibis*, **150**:27–36.

24   Newey, S., Mustin, K., Bryce, R., Fielding, D. & Redpath, S. (2016).
      Impact of Management on Avian Communities in the Scottish Highlands.
      PLoS ONE, **11**:e0155473.

25   Whitehead, S.C., Hesford, N. & Baines, D. (2018). Changes in the
      abundance of some ground-nesting birds on moorland in South
      West Scotland. *Research Report to Scottish Land & Estates and Scottish
      Gamekeepers Association*. Fordingbridge.

26   Aebischer, N.J., Ewald, J.A. & Tapper, S.C. (2010). Driven grouse
      shooting in Britain: a form of upland management with wider
      conservation benefits. In: *Proceedings of the World Symposium on Hunting
      Activities: Ecologic and Economic Benefits of Hunting*: 186–201.

27   Warren, P. & Baines, D. (2014). Changes in the abundance and distribution of upland breeding birds in the Berwyn Special Protection Area, North Wales 1983-2002. *Birds in Wales*, **11**:32–42.

28   Smith, A.A., Redpath, S.M., Campbell, S.T. & Thirgood, S.J. (2001). Meadow pipits, red grouse and the habitat characteristics of managed grouse moors. *Journal of Applied Ecology*, **38**:390–400.

29   Whitfield, D.P., Fielding, A.H., McLeod, D.R.A. & Haworth, P.F. (2004). The effects of persecution on age of breeding and territory occupation in golden eagles in Scotland. *Biological Conservation*, **118**:249–259.

30   Whitfield, D.P., Fielding, A.H., McLeod, D.R.A., Haworth, P.F. & Watson, J. (2006). A conservation framework for the golden eagle in Scotland: refining condition targets and assessment of constraint influences. *Biological Conservation*, **130**:465–480.

31   Etheridge, B., Summers, R.W. & Green, R.E. (1997). The effects of illegal killing and destruction of nests by humans on the population dynamics of the Hen Harrier *Circus cyaneus* in Scotland. *Journal of Applied Ecology*, **34**:1081–1105.

32   Amar, A., Court, I.R., Davison, M., Downing, S., Grimshaw, T., Pickford, T. & Raw, D. (2012). Linking nest histories, remotely sensed land use data and wildlife crime records to explore the impact of grouse moor management on peregrine falcon populations. *Biological Conservation*, **145**:86–94.

33   Newton, I. (1979). *Population ecology of raptors.* T&AD Poyser. Berkhampstead.

34   Fielding, A., Haworth, P., Whitfield, P., McLeod, D. & Riley, H. (2011). A conservation framework for hen harriers in the United Kingdom. *JNCC Report 441.* Joint Nature Conservation Committee, Peterborough.

35   Fielding, A.H. & Haworth, P.F. (2014). *Golden eagles in the south of Scotland: an overview.*

36   Baines, D. & Richardson, M. (2013). Hen harriers on a Scottish grouse moor: multiple factors predict breeding density and productivity. *Journal of Applied Ecology*, **50**:1397–1405.

37   Ludwig, S., Roos, S., Bubb, D. & Baines, D. (2017). Long-term trends in abundance and breeding success of red grouse and hen harriers in relation to changing management of a Scottish grouse moor. *Wildlife Biology*, wlb.00246:1-7.

38   Murgatroyd, M., Redpath, S.M., Murphy, S.G., Douglas, D.J.T., Saunders, R. & Amar, A. (2019). Patterns of satellite tagged hen harrier disappearances suggest widespread illegal killing on British grouse moors. *Nature Communications*, **10**:1094.

39   Ludwig, S.C., Roos, S. & Baines, D. (2019). Long-term changes in the abundance and breeding success of raptors and ravens in periods of varying management of a Scottish grouse moor. *Submitted,*

40   Rogers, S. (2014). Merlin Study Report. *Report to the Moorland Association.* Penny Anderson Associates, Buxton.

41   Brown, D., Wilson, J., Douglas, D., Thompson, P., Foster, S., McCulloch, N., Phillips, J., Stroud, D., Whitehead, S., Crockford, N. & Sheldon, R. (2015). The Eurasian curlew - the most pressing bird conservation priority in the UK? *British Birds,* **108**:660–668.

42   BirdLife International. (2019). Species factsheet: *Numenius arquata.* Available at: http://datazone.birdlife.org/species/factsheet/eurasian-curlew-numenius-arquata.

43   Wilson, A.M., Vickery, J.A., Brown, A., Langston, R.H.W., Smallshire, D., Wotton, S. & Vanhinsbergh, D. (2005). Changes in the numbers of breeding waders on lowland wet grasslands in England and Wales between 1982 and 2002. *Bird Study,* **52**:55–69.

44   Balmer, D., Gillings, S.D., Caffrey, B., Swann, B., Downie, I. & Fuller, R. (2013). *Bird Atlas 2007-11: the breeding and wintering birds of Britain and Ireland.* BTO Books.

45   Warren, P., Atterton, F., Baines, D., Viel, M., Deal, Z., Richardson, M. & Newborn, D. (2015). Numbers and distribution of black grouse *Tetrao tetrix* males in England: results from the fourth survey in 2014. *Bird Study,* **62**:202–207.

46   Warren, P. & Baines, D. (2004). Black grouse in northern England: stemming the decline. *British Birds,* **97**:183–189.

47   Baines, D. (1996). The implications of grazing and predator management on the habitats and breeding success of black grouse *Tetrao tetrix. Journal of Applied Ecology,* **33**:54–62.

48   Moss, R. (1986). Rain, breeding success and distribution of capercaillie *Tetrao urogallus* and black grouse *Tetrao tetrix* in Scotland. *Ibis,* **128**:65–72.

49   Warren, P., White, P.J.C., Baines, D., Atterton, F. & Brown, M.J. (2013). Variations in black grouse *Tetrao tetrix* winter survival in a year with prolonged snow cover. *Bird Study,* **60**:257–263.

50   Hesford, N., Fletcher, K., Howarth, D., Smith, A.A., Aebischer, N.J. & Baines, D. (2019). Spatial and temporal variation in mountain hare (*Lepus timidus*) abundance in relation to red grouse (*Lagopus lagopus scotica*) management in Scotland. *European Journal of Wildlife Research,* **65**:1-7 doi: 10.1007/s10344-019-1273-7.

51   Flux, J.E.C. (1970). Life history of the mountain hare (*Lepus timidus*

scoticus) in north-east Scotland. *Journal of Zoology*, **161**:75–123.

52 Watson, A. & Wilson, J.D. (2018). Seven decades of mountain hare counts show severe declines where high-yield recreational game bird hunting is practised. *Journal of Applied Ecology*, **55**:1–10.

53 Mackey, E., Shewry, M. & Tudor, G. (1999). *Land cover change: Scotland from the 1940s to the 1980s*. The Stationary Office. Edinburgh.

54 Grau-Andrés, R., Davies, G.M., Waldron, S., Scott, E.M. & Gray, A. (2017). Leaving moss and litter layers undisturbed reduces the short-term environmental consequences of heathland managed burns. *Journal of Environmental Management*, **204**:102–110.

55 Grau-Andrés, R., Davies, G.M., Waldron, S., Scott, E.M. & Gray, A. (2019). Increased fire severity alters initial vegetation regeneration across *Calluna*-dominated ecosystems. *Journal of Environmental Management*, **231**:1004–1011.

56 Hancock, M.H., Amphlett, A., Proctor, R., Dugan, D., Willi, J., Harvey, P. & Summers, R.W. (2011). Burning and mowing as habitat management for capercaillie *Tetrao urogallus*: an experimental test. *Forest Ecology and Management*, **262**:509–521.

57 Miller, G.R. (1979). Quantity and quality of the annual production of shoots and flowers by *Calluna vulgaris* in North-East Scotland. *Journal of Ecology*, **69**:109–129.

58 Gardner, S.M., Liepert, C. & Rees, S. (1993). Managing heather moorland: impacts of burning and cutting on *calluna* regeneration. *Journal of Environmental Planning and Management*, **36**:283–293.

59 Buchanan, G.M., Grant, M.C., Sanderson, R.A. & Pearce-Higgins, J.W. (2006). The contribution of invertebrate taxa to moorland bird diets and the potential implications of land-use management. *Ibis*: **148**:615–628.

60 Miller, G.R. (1980). The burning of heather moorland for red grouse. *Bulletin of Ecology*, **11**:725–733.

61 The Muirburn Code. (2017). Management of moorland by fire and cutting. Available at: http://muirburncode.org.uk/.

62 Natural England. (2019). Burning as a tool for the restoration of upland blanket bog: position statement by Natural England. Available at: http://publications.naturalengland.org.uk/publication/6647144950005760.

63 Allen, K.A., Denelle, P., Ruiz, F.M.S., Santana, V.M. & Marrs, R.H. (2016). Prescribed moorland burning meets good practice guidelines: a monitoring case study using aerial photography in the Peak District, UK. *Ecological Indicators*, **62**:79–85.

64 MacDonald, A.J., Kirkpatrick, A.H., Hester, A.J. & Sydes, C. (1995).

Regeneration by natural layering of heather (*Calluna vulgaris*): frequency and characteristics in upland Britain. *Journal of Applied Ecology*, **32**:85–99.

65   Glaves, D., Morecroft, M., Fitzgibbon, C., Owen, M., Phillips, S. & Leppitt, P. (2013). Natural England review of upland evidence 2012 - the effects of managed burning on upland peatland biodiversity, carbon and water. *Natural England Evidence Review, Number 004.*

66   Werritty, A., Pakeman, R., Shedden, C., Smith, A. & Wilson, J. (2015). *A Review of Sustainable Moorland Management. Report to the Scientific Advisory Committee of Scottish Natural Heritage.*

67   Welch, D. (2016). The floristic changes of Scottish moorland dominated by heather (*Calluna vulgaris*, Ericaceae) but unburnt for 50 years and kept checked by moderate grazing. *New Journal of Botany*, **6**:31–42.

68   Franks, S.E., Douglas, D.J.T., Gillings, S. & Pearce-Higgins, J.W. (2017). Environmental correlates of breeding abundance and population change of Eurasian curlew *Numenius arquata* in Britain. *Bird Study*, **64**:DOI: 10.1080/00063657.2017.1359233.

69   Pearce-Higgins, J.W. & Yalden, D.W. (2004). Habitat selection, diet, arthropod availability and growth of a moorland wader: the ecology of European golden plover *Pluvialis apricaria* chicks. *Ibis*, **146**:335–346.

70   Usher, M.B. & Thompson, D.B.A. (1993). Variation in the upland heathlands of Great Britain: conservation importance. *Biological Conservation*, **66**:69–81.

71   Bokdam, J. & Gleichman, J.M. (2000). Effects of grazing by free-ranging cattle on vegetation dynamics in a continental north-west European heathland. *Journal of Applied Ecology*, **37**:415–431.

72   Gillingham, P., Stewart, J. & Binney, H. (2016). The historic peat record: implications for the restoration of blanket bog. *Natural England Evidence Review, Number 011.*

73   Shepherd, M.J., Labadz, J., Caporn, S.J., Crowle, A., Goodison, R., Rebane, M. & Waters, R. (2013). Natural England review of upland evidence - restoration of degraded blanket bog. *Natural England Evidence Review, Number 003.*

74   Lee, H., Alday, J.G., Rose, R.J., O'Reilly, J. & Marrs, R.H. (2013). Long-term effects of rotational prescribed burning and low-intensity sheep grazing on blanket-bog plant communities. *Journal of Applied Ecology*, **50**:625–635.

75   Whitehead, S.C. & Baines, D. (2018). Moorland vegetation responses following prescribed burning on blanket peat. *International Journal of Wildland Fire*, **27**:658–664.

76   Milligan, G., Rose, R.J., O'Reilly, J. & Marrs, R.H. (2018). Effects of

rotational prescribed burning and sheep grazing on moorland plant communities: results from a 60-year intervention experiment. *Land Degradation and Development*, **29**:1397–1412.

77   Noble, A., O'Reilly, J., Glaves, D.J., Crowle, A., Palmer, S.M. & Holden, J. (2018). Impacts of prescribed burning on *Sphagnum* mosses in a long-term peatland field experiment. *PLoS ONE*, **13**:e0206320.

78   Garnett, M.H., Ineson, P. & Stevenson, A.C. (2000). Effects of burning and grazing on carbon sequestration in a Pennine blanket bog, UK. *Holocene*, **10**:729–736.

79   Ashby, M.A. & Heinemeyer, A. (2019). Prescribed burning impacts on ecosystem services in the British uplands: a methodological critique of the EMBER project. *Journal of Applied Ecology*, **00**:1–9. https://doi.org/10.1111/1365-2664.13476

80   Taylor, E.S., Levy, P.E. & Gray, A. (2017). The recovery of *Sphagnum capillifolium* following exposure to temperatures of simulated moorland fires: a glasshouse experiment. *Plant Ecology and Diversity*, **10**:77–88.

81   Grau-Andrés, R., Davies, G.M., Gray, A., Scott, E.M. & Waldron, S. (2018). Fire severity is more sensitive to low fuel moisture content on *Calluna* heathlands than on peat bogs. *Science of the Total Environment*, **616**:1261–1269.

82   Bold, H.C. (1967). *Morphology of Plants*. Harper and Row. New York.

83   Hájek, T., Ballance, S., Limpens, J., Zijlstra, M. & Verhoeven, J.T.A. (2011). Cell-wall polysaccharides play an important role in decay resistance of *Sphagnum* and actively depressed decomposition *in vitro*. *Biogeochemistry*, **103**:45–57.

84   Morton, P.A. & Heinemeyer, A. (2019). Bog breathing: the extent of peat shrinkage and expansion on blanket bogs in relation to water table, heather management and dominant vegetation and its implications for carbon stock assessments. *Wetlands Ecology and Management*, https://doi.org/10.1007/s11273-019-09672-5

85   Larmola, T., Tuittila, E.S., Tiirola, M., Nykänen, H., Martikainen, P.J., Yrjälä, K., Tuomivirta, T. & Fritze, H. (2010). The role of *Sphagnum* mosses in the methane cycling of a boreal mire. *Ecology*, **91**:2356–2365.

86   BBC News. (2017). Gamekeepers playing part in wildfire prevention. Available at: https://www.bbc.co.uk/news/uk-scotland-highlands-islands-39653033.

87   Allen, K.A., Harris, M.P.K. & Marrs, R.H. (2013). Matrix modelling of prescribed burning in *Calluna vulgaris*-dominated moorland: short burning rotations minimize carbon loss at increased wildfire frequencies. *Journal of Applied Ecology*, **50**:614–624.

88   IUCN peatlands programme. (2019). UK Peatlands. Available at: https://www.iucn-uk-peatlandprogramme.org/about-peatlands/uk-peatlands.

89   Moore, P.D. (1989). The ecology of peat-forming processes: a review. *International Journal of Coal Geology*, **12**:89–103.

90   Clay, G.D., Worrall, F. & Rose, R. (2010). Carbon budgets of an upland blanket bog managed by prescribed fire. *Journal of Geophysical Research: Biogeosciences*, **115**:G04037.

91   Garnett, M.H., Ineson, P. & Stevenson, A.C. (2000). Effects of burning and grazing on carbon sequestration in a Pennine blanket bog, UK. *Holocene*, **10**:729–736.

92   Farage, P., Ball, A., Mcgenity, T.J., Whitby, C. & Pretty, J. (2009). Burning management and carbon sequestration of upland heather moorland in the UK. *Australian Journal of Soil Research*, **47**:351–361.

93   Heinemeyer, A., Asena, Q., Burn, W.L. & Jones, A.L. (2018). Peatland carbon stocks and burn history: blanket bog peat core evidence highlights charcoal impacts on peat physical properties and long-term carbon storage. *Geo: Geography and Environment*, **5**:e00063.

94   Evans, C.D., Baird, A.J., Green, S.M., Page, S.E., Peacock, M., Reed, M.S., Rose, N.L., Stoneman, R., Thom, T.J., Young, D.M. & Garnett, M.H. (2019). Comment on: "Peatland carbon stocks and burn history: blanket bog peat core evidence highlights charcoal impacts on peat physical properties and long-term carbon storage," by A. Heinemeyer, Q. Asena, W. L. Burn and A. L. Jones. *Geo: Geography and Environment*, **00**:e00075.

95   Heinemeyer, A., Burn, W.L., Asena, Q., Jones, A.L. & Ashby, M.A. (2019). Response to: Comment on "Peatland carbon stocks and burn history: Blanket bog peat core evidence highlights charcoal impacts on peat physical properties and long-term carbon storage" by Evans et al. *Geo: Geography and Environment*, **00**:e00078.

96   Clay, G.D. & Worrall, F. (2011). Charcoal production in a UK moorland wildfire - how important is it? *Journal of Environmental Management*, **92**:676–682.

97   O'Connell, S. (2017). *UK natural capital: developing UK mountain, moorland and heathland ecosystem accounts*.

98   Clay, G.D., Worrall, F. & Aebischer, N.J. (2012). Does prescribed burning on peat soils influence DOC concentrations in soil and runoff waters? Results from a 10 year chronosequence. *Journal of Hydrology*, **448–449**:139–148.

99   Evans, C.D., Malcolm, I.A., Shilland, E.M., Rose, N.L., Turner, S.D., Crilly, A., Norris, D., Granath, G. & Monteith, D.T. (2017). Sustained

biogeochemical impacts of wildfire in a mountain lake catchment. *Ecosystems*, **20**:813–829.

100 Holden, J., Palmer, S.M., Johnston, K., Wearing, C., Irvine, B. & Brown, L.E. (2015). Impact of prescribed burning on blanket peat hydrology. *Water Resources Research*, **51**:6472–6484.

101 Martin, D., Fraser, M., Pakeman, R. & Moffatt, A. (2013). Impact of moorland grazing and stocking rates.*Natural England Review of Upland Evidence 2012*

102 Albertson, K., Aylen, J., Cavan, G. & McMorrow, J. (2010). Climate change and the future occurrence of moorland wildfires in the Peak District of the UK. *Climate Research*, **45**:105–118.

103 McMorrow, J., Lindley, S., Aylen, J., Cavan, G., Albertson, K. & Boys, D. (2009). Moorland wildfire risk, visitors and climate change: patterns, prevention and policy. In: *Drivers of Change in Upland Environments*: 404–431. (eds. Bonn, A., Allott, K., Hubacek, K. & Stewart, J.) Routledge. Abingdon.

104 Boer, M., Sadler, R., Wittkuhn, R. & McCaw, L. (2009). Long-term impacts of prescribed burning on regional extent and incidence of wildfires - evidence from 50 years of active fire management in SW Australian forests. *Forest Ecology and Management*, **259**: 132-142.

105 Holden, J., Shotbolt, L., Bonn, A., Burt, T.P., Chapman, P.J., Dougill, A.J., Fraser, E.D.G., Hubacek, K., Irvine, B., Kirkby, M.J., Reed, M.S., Prell, C., Stagl, S., Stringer, L.C., Turner, A. & Worrall, F. (2007). Environmental change in moorland landscapes. *Earth-Science Reviews*, **82**:75–100.

106 Davies, G.M., Kettridge, N., Stoof, C.R., Gray, A., Ascoli, D., Fernandes, P.M., Marrs, R., Allen, K.A., Doerr, S.H., Clay, G.D., McMorrow, J. & Vandvik, V. (2016). The role of fire in UK peatland and moorland management: the need for informed, unbiased debate. *Philosophical Transactions of the Royal Society of London B: Biological Sciences*, **371**: 20150342. http://dx.doi.org/10.1098/rstb.2015.0342

107 Davies, G.M., Gray, A., Rein, G. & Legg, C.J. (2013). Peat consumption and carbon loss due to smouldering wildfire in a temperate peatland. *Forest Ecology and Management*, **308**:169–177.

108 Parliamentary Office of Science and Technology. (2019). *Climate Change and UK Wildfire. POSTNOTE 603.*

109 Uplands Management Group. (2019). Wildfire Risk Assessment. Available at: https://docs.wixstatic.com/ugd/fdc287_0646cebac630453bb-0c71eb50d8fb592.pdf.

110 Brown, L.E., Holden, J. & Palmer, S.M. (2016). Moorland vegetation

burning debates should avoid contextomy and anachronism: a comment on Davies et al . (2016). *Philosophical Transactions of the Royal Society B: Biological Sciences*, **371**:20160432.

111   Douglas, D.J.T., Buchanan, G.M., Thompson, P. & Wilson, J.D. (2016). The role of fire in UK upland management: the need for informed challenge to conventional wisdoms: a comment on Davies *et al.* (2016). *Philosophical Transactions of the Royal Society B: Biological Sciences*, **371**:20160433.

112   Davies, G.M., Kettridge, N., Stoof, C.R., Gray, A., Marrs, R., Ascoli, D., Fernandes, P.M., Allen, K.A., Doerr, S.H., Clay, G.D., McMorrow, J. & Vandvik, V. (2016). The peatland vegetation burning debate: keep scientific critique in perspective. A response to Brown et al. and Douglas et al. *Philosophical Transactions of the Royal Society of London B: Biological Sciences*, **371**: 20160434.

113   Chesterton, C. (2009). Environmental impacts of land management. *Natural England Research Report NERR030.*

114   Coulson, J.C., Butterfield, J.E.L. & Henderson, E. (1990). The effect of open drainage ditches on the plant and invertebrate communities of moorland and on the decomposition of peat. *Journal of Applied Ecology*, **27**:549–561.

115   Holden, J. (2004). Artificial drainage of peatlands: hydrological and hydrochemical process and wetland restoration. *Progress in Physical Geography*, **28**:95–123.

116   Watson, A. & Miller, G.R. (1976). Grouse Management. *The Game Conservancy Green Guide, Booklet 12*. Fordingbridge.

117   Ramchunder, S.J., Brown, L.E. & Holden, J. (2009). Environmental effects of drainage, drain-blocking and prescribed vegetation burning in UK upland peatlands. *Progress in Physical Geography*, **33**:49–79.

118   Worrall, F., Armstrong, A. & Holden, J. (2007). Short-term impact of peat drain-blocking on water colour, dissolved organic carbon concentration, and water table depth. *Journal of Hydrology*, **337**:315–325.

119   Wallage, Z.E., Holden, J. & McDonald, A.T. (2006). Drain blocking: an effective treatment for reducing dissolved organic carbon loss and water discolouration in a drained peatland. *Science of the Total Environment*, **367**:811–821.

120   The Moorland Association. (2016). Highs and lows for start of grouse season. Available at: http://www.moorlandassociation.org/2016/08/highs-lows-start-grouse-season/.

121   Armstrong, A., Holden, J., Kay, P., Foulger, M., Gledhill, S., McDonald, A.T. & Walker, A. (2009). Drain-blocking techniques on blanket peat:

a framework for best practice. *Journal of Environmental Management*, **90**:3512–3519.

122   UK National Ecosystem Assessment. (2011). *The UK National Ecosystem Assessment Technical Report. Cambridge.*

123   Bellamy, P.E., Stephen, L., Maclean, I.S. & Grant, M.C. (2012). Response of blanket bog vegetation to drain-blocking. *Applied Vegetation Science*, **15**:129–135.

124   Potts, G.R., Tapper, S.C. & Hudson, P.J. (1984). Population fluctuations in red grouse: analysis of bag records and a simulation model. *Journal of Animal Ecology*, **53**:21–36.

125   Hudson, P.J., Dobson, A.P. & Newborn, D. (1992). Do parasites make prey vulnerable to predation? Red grouse and parasites. *Journal of Animal Ecology*, **61**:681–692.

126   Leslie, A.S. & Shipley, A.E. (2011). *The grouse in health and disease.* Smith, Elder & Co. London.

127   Hudson, P. (1992). *Grouse in space and time. The population biology of a managed gamebird.* The Game Conservancy Trust. Fordingbridge.

128   Hudson, P.J. (1986). The effect of a parasitic nematode on the breeding production of red grouse. *Journal of Animal Ecology*, **55**:85–92.

129   Hudson, P.J., Dobson, a P. & Newborn, D. (1998). Prevention of population cycles by parasite removal. *Science (New York, N.Y.)*, **282**:2256–2258.

130   Newborn, D. & Foster, R. (2002). Control of parasite burdens in wild red grouse *Lagopus lagopus scoticus* through the indirect application of anthelmintics. *Journal of Applied Ecology*, **39**:909–914.

131   Baines, D., Newborn, D. & Richardson, M. (2019). Are *Trichostrongylus tenuis* control and resistance avoidance simultaneously manageable by reducing anthelmintic intake by grouse? *Veterinary Record*, 1-8. doi: 10.1136/vr.105029.

132   Cox, R., Newborn, D., Baines, D., Thomas, C.J. & Sherratt, T.N. (2010). No evidence for resistance to fenbendazole in *Trichostrongylus tenuis*, a nematode parasite of the red grouse. *Journal of Wildlife Management*, **74**:1799–1805.

133   Abbott, K.A., Taylor, M. & Stubbings, L.A. (2012). *Sustainable worm control strategies for sheep 4th Edition. A technical manual for veterinary surgeons and advisors.*

134   European Medicines Agency. Veterinary medicines and inspections. (2004). *Committee for veterinary medicinal products. Flubendazole.*

135   Jeffries, C.L., Mansfield, K.L., Phipps, L.P., Wakeley, P.R., Mearns, R.,

Schock, A., Bell, S., Breed, A.C., Fooks, A.R. & Johnson, N. (2014). Louping ill virus: an endemic tick-borne disease of Great Britain. *Journal of General Virology*, **95**:1005–1014.

136 Reid, H.W. (1975). Experimental infection of red grouse with louping-ill virus (Flavivirus group). I. The viraemia and antibody response. *Journal of Comparative Pathology*, **85**:223–229.

137 Buxton, D. & Reid, H.W. (1975). Experimental infection of red grouse with louping-ill virus (Flavivirus group). II. Neuropathology. *Journal of Comparative Pathology*, **85**:231–235.

138 Grant, M.C., Orsman, C., Easton, J., Lodge, C., Smith, M., Thompson, G., Rodwell, S. & Moore, N. (1999). Breeding success and causes of breeding failure of curlew *Numenius arquata* in Northern Ireland. *Journal of Applied Ecology*, **36**:59–74.

139 Newborn, D., Fletcher, K., Beeston, R. & Baines, D. (2009). Occurrence of sheep ticks on moorland wader chicks. *Bird Study*, **56**:401–404.

140 Baines, D., Becker, M. & Hart, S. (2019). Sheep tick *Ixodes ricinus* management on Welsh hill farms of designated conservation importance: implications for nationally declining birds. *Medical and Veterinary Entomology*, DOI: 10.1111/mve.12368.

141 Kirby, A.D., Smith, A.A., Benton, T.G. & Hudson, P.J. (2004). Rising burden of immature sheep ticks (*Ixodes ricinus*) on red grouse (*Lagopus lagopus scoticus*) chicks in the Scottish uplands. *Medical and Veterinary Entomology*, **18**:67–70.

142 Scharlemann, J.P.W., Johnson, P.J., Smith, A.A., Macdonald, D.W. & Randolph, S.E. (2008). Trends in *ixodid* tick abundance and distribution in Great Britain. *Medical and Veterinary Entomology*, **22**:238–247.

143 Newborn, D. & Baines, D. (2012). Enhanced control of sheep ticks in upland sheep flocks: repercussions for red grouse co-hosts. *Medical and Veterinary Entomology*, **26**:63–69.

144 Fletcher, K. & Baines, D. (2018). The effects of acaricide treatment of sheep on red grouse *Lagopus lagopus scotica* tick burdens and productivity in a multi-host system. *Medical and Veterinary Entomology*, **32**:235–243.

145 Laurenson, M.K., Norman, R.A., Gilbert, L., Reid, H.W. & Hudson, P.J. (2003). Identifying disease reservoirs in complex systems: mountain hares as reservoirs of ticks and louping-ill virus, pathogens of red grouse. *Journal of Animal Ecology*, **72**:177–185.

146 Harrison, A., Newey, S., Gilbert, L., Haydon, D.T. & Thirgood, S. (2010). Culling wildlife hosts to control disease: mountain hares, red grouse and louping ill virus. *Journal of Applied Ecology*, **47**:926–930.

147 Gilbert, L., Maffey, G.L., Ramsay, S.L. & Hester, A.J. (2012). The effect

of deer management on the abundance of *Ixodes ricinus* in Scotland. *Ecological Applications*, **22**:658–667.

148   Laurenson, M.K., Hudson, P.J., McGuire, K., Thirgood, S.J. & Reid, H.W. (1997). Efficacy of acaricidal tags and pour-on as prophylaxis against ticks and louping-ill in red grouse. *Medical and Veterinary Entomology*, **11**:389–393.

149   Mougeot, F., Moseley, M., Leckie, F., Martinez-Padilla, J., Miller, A., Pounds, M. & Irvine, R.J. (2008). Reducing tick burdens on chicks by treating breeding female grouse with permethrin. *Journal of Wildlife Management*, **72**:468–472.

150   Baines, D. & Taylor, L. (2016). Can acaricide-impregnated leg bands fitted to female red grouse reduce sheep tick parasitization of chicks and increase chick survival? *Medical and Veterinary Entomology*, **30**:360–364.

151   Porter, R., Norman, R.A. & Gilbert, L. (2013). A model to test how ticks and louping ill virus can be controlled by treating red grouse with acaricide. *Medical and Veterinary Entomology*, **27**:237–246.

152   Coldwell, L., Caldow, G., Holliman, A., Mearns, R., Errington, H., Giles, M., Willoughby, K. & Wood, A. (2012). *Cryptospordium baileyi* in wild red grouse with 'bulgy eye'. *Veterinary Record*, **34**:603–604.

153   Baines, D., Newborn, D. & Richardson, M. (2014). Short Communication spread of *Cryptosporidium baileyi* in red grouse (*Lagopus lagopus scoticus*). *Veterinary Record*, **175**:149 (doi: 10.1136/vr.102275).

154   Baines, D., Giles, M. & Richardson, M. (2017). Microscopic and molecular tracing of *Cryptosporidium* oocysts: identifying a possible reservoir of infection in red grouse. *Pathogens*, **6**:57–61.

155   Baines, D., Allinson, H., Duff, J.P., Fuller, H., Newborn, D. & Richardson, M. (2018). Lethal and sub-lethal impacts of respiratory cryptosporidiosis on red grouse, a wild gamebird of economic importance. *Ibis*, **160**:882–891.

156   Tapper, S.C., Potts, G.R. & Brockless, M.H. (1996). The effect of an experimental reduction in predation pressure on the breeding success and population density of grey partridges *Perdix perdix*. *Journal of Applied Ecology*, **33**:965–978.

157   Roodbergen, M., van der Werf, B. & Hotker, H. (2012). Revealing the contributions of reproduction and survival to the Europe-wide decline in meadow birds: review and meta-analysis. *Journal of Ornithology*: **153**:53–74.

158   Birdlife International. (2015). European Red List of birds. http://www.birdlife.org/datazone/userfiles/file/Sp.

159   Aebischer, N.J. (2009). Gamebird science, agricultural policy and

biodiversity conservation in lowland areas of the UK. In: *Recreational Hunting, Conservation and Rural Livelihoods - Science and Practice*: 197–211. (eds. Dickson, B., Hutton, J. & Adams, W.M.) Blackwell Publishing Ltd. Oxford.

160   Sotherton, N.W., Baines, D. & Aebischer, N.J. (2017). An alternative view of moorland management for red grouse *Lagopus lagopus scotica*. *Ibis*, **159**:693–698.

161   Roos, S., Smart, J., Gibbons, D.W. & Wilson, J.D. (2018). A review of predation as a limiting factor for bird populations in mesopredator-rich landscapes: a case study of the UK. *Biological Reviews*, **93**:1915–1937.

162   Smith, R.K., Pullin, A.S., Stewart, G.B. & Sutherland, W.J. (2010). Effectiveness of predator removal for enhancing bird populations. *Conservation Biology*, **24**:820–829.

163   Aebischer, N., Baines, D., Ewald, J., Jones, C., Fletcher, K., Foster, R., Hoodless, A., Sotherton, N. & Tapper, S. (2010). *Waders on the Fringe*. Game and Wildlife Conservation Trust.

164   Redpath, S.M. (1991). The impact of hen harriers on red grouse breeding success. *Journal of Applied Ecology*, **28**:659–671.

165   Redpath, S.M. & Thirgood, S.J. (1999). Numerical and functional responses in generalist predators: hen harriers and peregrines on Scottish grouse moors. *Journal of Animal Ecology*, **68**:879–892.

166   Redpath, S.M., Thirgood, S.J. & Clarke, R. (2002). Field vole *Microtus agrestis* abundance and hen harrier *Circus cyaneus* diet and breeding in Scotland. *Ibis*, **144**:E33–E38.

167   Redpath, S.M. & Thirgood, S.J. (1997). *Birds of prey and red grouse*. Stationary Office. London.

168   Countryside Alliance & The National Gamekeepers Organisation. (2015). *The value of grouse moor management*.

169   Thirgood, S.J., Redpath, S.M., Rothery, P. & Aebischer, N.J. (2000). Raptor predation and population limitation in red grouse. *Journal of Animal Ecology*, **69**:504–516.

170   Tapper, S. (2005). *Hen harriers and the Joint Raptor Study*. Fordingbridge.

171   Potts, G. (1998). Global dispersion of nesting hen harriers *Circus cyaneus*; implications for grouse moors in the UK. *Ibis*, **140**:76–88.

172   Wotton, S.R., Bladwell, S., Mattingley, W., Morris, N.G., Raw, D., Ruddock, M., Stevenson, A. & Eaton, M.A. (2018). Status of the hen harrier *Circus cyaneus* in the UK and Isle of Man in 2016. *Bird Study*, **65**:145–160.

173   Sim, I.M.W., Dillon, I.A., Eaton, M.A., Etheridge, B., Lindley, P.,

Riley, H., Saunders, R., Sharpe, C. & Tickner, M. (2007). Status of the hen harrier *Circus cyaneus* in the UK and Isle of Man in 2004, and a comparison with the 1988/89 and 1998 surveys. *Bird Study*, **54**:256–267.

174   McMillan, R. (2014). Hen Harriers on Skye, 2000–12: nest failures and predation. *Scottish Birds*, **34**:30-39.

175   Thirgood, S. & Redpath, S. (1997). Red grouse and their predators. *Nature*, **390**:547.

176   Thirgood, S.J., Redpath, S.M., Campbell, S. & Smith, A.A. (2002). Do habitat characteristics influence predation on red grouse? *Journal of Applied Ecology*, **39**:217–225.

177   Natural England & Defra. (2019). Record-breaking year for hen harrier breeding Available at: https://www.gov.uk/government/news/record-breaking-year-for-hen-harrier-breeding.

178   Redpath, S., Madders, M., Donnelly, E., Anderson, B., Thirgood, S., Martin, A. & McLeod, D. (1998). Nest site selection by hen harriers in Scotland. *Bird Study*, **45**:51–61.

179   Amar, A. & Redpath, S.M. (2005). Habitat use by hen harriers *Circus cyaneus* on Orkney: implications of land-use change for this declining population. *Ibis*, **147**:37–47.

180   Wilson, M.W., Fernández-Bellon, D., Irwin, S. & O'Halloran, J. (2017). Hen harrier *Circus cyaneus* population trends in relation to wind farms. *Bird Study*, **64**:20–29.

181   Pearce-Higgins, J.W., Stephen, L., Langston, R.H.W., Bainbridge, I.P. & Bullman, R. (2009). The distribution of breeding birds around upland wind farms. *Journal of Applied Ecology*, **46**:1323–1331.

182   Elston, D.A., Spezia, L., Baines, D. & Redpath, S.M. (2014). Working with stakeholders to reduce conflict - modelling the impact of varying hen harrier *Circus cyaneus* densities on red grouse *Lagopus lagopus* populations. *Journal of Applied Ecology*, **51**:1236–1245.

183   Redpath, S., Amar, A. & Smith, A. (2010). People and nature in conflict: can we reconcile hen harrier conservation and game management. In: *Species Management: Challenges and Solution for the 21st Century:* Chapter 18. (eds. Baxter, J. & Galbraith, C..) Edinburgh.

184   Thompson, P.S., Amar, A., Hoccom, D.G., Knott, J. & Wilson, J.D. (2009). Resolving the conflict between driven-grouse shooting and conservation of hen harriers. *Journal of Applied Ecology*, **46**:950–954.

185   Thirgood, S. & Redpath, S. (2008). Hen harriers and red grouse: science, politics and human-wildlife conflict. *Journal of Applied Ecology*: **45**:1550–1554.

186   Thirgood, S., Redpath, S., Newton, I. & Hudson, P. (2000). Raptors

and red grouse: conservation conflicts and management solutions. *Conservation Biology*, **14**:95–104.

187   Redpath, S. & Thirgood, S. (2009). Hen harriers and red grouse: moving towards consensus? *Journal of Applied Ecology*, **46**:961–963.

188   Langholm Moor Demonstration Project, Langholm, 2014. (2014). *The Langholm Moor Demonstration Project: seven year review.*

189   Redpath, S.M., Thirgood, S.J. & Leckie, F.M. (2001). Does supplementary feeding reduce predation of red grouse by hen harriers? *Journal of Applied Ecology*, **38**:1157–1168.

190   Ludwig, S.C., Aebischer, N.J., Bubb, D., Roos, S. & Baines, D. (2018). Survival of chicks and adults explains variation in population growth in a recovering red grouse *Lagopus lagopus scotica* population. *Wildlife Biology*, wlb.00430: 1-10. doi: 10.2981/wlb.00430.

191   Ludwig, S.C., McCluskie, A., Keane, P., Barlow, C., Francksen, R.M., Bubb, D., Roos, S., Aebischer, N.J. & Baines, D. (2018). Diversionary feeding and nestling diet of hen harriers *Circus cyaneus. Bird Study*, **65**:431–443.

192   Francksen RM, Aebischer NJ, Ludwig SC, Baines D, Whittingham MJ (2019) Measures of predator diet alone may underestimate the collective impact on prey: Common buzzard *Buteo buteo* consumption of economically important red grouse *Lagopus lagopus scotica. PLoS ONE* **14(8)**: e0221404. https://doi.org/10.1371/journal.pone.0221404

193   Francksen, R.M., Whittingham, M.J. & Baines, D. (2016). Assessing prey provisioned to common buzzard *Buteo buteo* chicks: a comparison of methods. *Bird Study*, **63**:303–310.

194   Francksen, R.M., Whittingham, M.J., Ludwig, S.C. & Baines, D. (2016). Winter diet of common buzzard *Buteo buteo* on a Scottish grouse moor. *Bird Study*, **63**:525–532.

195   Uplands Stakeholder Forum. (2016). *Joint Action Plan to increase the English hen harrier population.*

196   Pomarol, M. (1994). Releasing Montagu's harrier (*Circus pygargus*) by the method of hacking. *Journal of Raptor Research*, **28**:19–22.

197   Arroyo, B., García, J.T. & Bretagnolle, V. (2002). Conservation of the Montagu's harrier (*Circus pygargus*) in agricultural areas. *Animal Conservation*, **5**:283–290.

198   Amar, A., Arroyo, B. & Bretagnolle, V. (2008). Post-fledging dependence and dispersal in hacked and wild Montagu's Harriers *Circus pygargus. Ibis*, **142**:21–28.

199   Brooker, R., Thomson, S., Matthews, K., Hester, A., Newey, S., Pakeman, R., Miller, D., Mell, V., Aalders, I., McMorran, R. & Glass, J. (2018).

Socioeconomic and biodiversity impacts of driven grouse moors in Scotland: Summary Report.

200 Stoddart, D.M. & Hewson, R. (1984). Mountain hare, *Lepus timidus*, bags and moor management. *Journal of Zoology*, **204**:563–565.

201 Mathews, F., Kubasiewicz, L.M., Gurnell, J., Harrower, C.A., McDonald, R.A. & Shore, R.F. (2018). A review of the population and conservation status of British mammals: technical summary. *A report by the Mammal Society under contract to Natural England, Natural Resources Wales and Scottish Natural Heritage.* Peterborough.

202 Newey, S., Fletcher, K., Potts, J. & Iason, G. (2018). Developing a counting methodology for mountain hares (*Lepus timidus*) in Scotland. *SNH Research Report 1022.*

203 Aebischer, N. (2019). Fifty-year trends in UK hunting bags of birds and mammals, and calibrated estimation of national bag size, using GWCT's National Gamebag Census. *European Journal of Wildlife Research*, **65**:64.

204 Massimino, D., Harris, S.J. & Gillings, S. (2018). Evaluating spatiotemporal trends in terrestrial mammal abundance using data collected during bird surveys. *Biological Conservation*, **226**:153–167.

205 Aebischer, N.J., Davey, P.D. & Kingdon, N.G. (2011). National Gamebag Census: Mammal Trends to 2009. *Game and Wildlife Conservation Trust*: Available at: https://www.gwct.org.uk/research/long-term-monitoring/national-gamebag-census/mammal-bags-comprehensive-overviews/fox/.

206 Wheeler, P.M., Ward, A.I., Smith, G.C., Croft, S. & Petrovan, S.O. (2019). Careful considerations are required when analysing mammal citizen science data – A response to Massimino *et al*. *Biological Conservation*, **232**:274–275.

207 Newey, S., Willebrand, T., Haydon, D.T., Dahl, F., Aebischer, N.J., Smith, A.A. & Thirgood, S.J. (2007). Do mountain hare populations cycle? *Oikos*, **116**:1547–1557.

208 Newey, S., Dahl, F., Willebrand, T. & Thirgood, S. (2007). Unstable dynamics and population limitation in mountain hares. *Biological Reviews*, **82**:527–549.

209 JNCC. (2013). The UK approach to assessing conservation status for the 2013 EU Habitats Directive Article 17 reporting. Peterborough.

210 Patton, V., Ewald, J.A., Smith, A.A., Newey, S.J., Iason, G.R., Thirgood, S.J. & Raynor, R. (2010). Distribution of mountain hares *Lepus timidus* in Scotland: results from a questionnaire. *Mammal Review*, **40**:313-326.

211 Iason, G.R., Hulbert, I.A.R., Hewson, R. & Dingerkus, K. (2008). Mountain hare/Irish hare *Lepus timidus*. In: *Mammals of the British Isles: Handbook*: 220–228. (eds. Harris, S. & Yalden, D.W.) Mammal Society.

London, UK.

212   Van der Wal, R., Bonn, A., Monteith, D., Reed, M., Blackstock, K., Hanley, N., Thompson, D., Evans, M., Alonso, I., Allott, T., Armitage, H., Beharry, N., Glass, J., Johnson, S., McMorrow, J., Ross, L., Pakeman, R., Perry, S. & Tinch, D. (2011). Mountains, Moorlands and Heaths. *UK National Ecosystem Assessment. Technical Report*, 105–160.

213   Smith, S., Gilbert, J., Bull, G., Gillam, S. & Whitton, S. (2010). National inventory of woodland and trees (1995–99): methodology. *Forestry Commission Research Report*. Edinburgh.

214   Scottish Forestry. (2019). Tree planting targets "smashed" says Ewing. Available at: https://forestry.gov.scot/news-releases/tree-planting-targets-smashed-say-ewing.

215   The Scottish Government. (2019). *Scotland's Forestry Strategy* 2019–2029.

216   Ratcliffe, D. (2007). *Galloway and the Borders*. Collins New Naturalist. London.

217   Marquiss, M., Newton, I. & Ratcliffe, D.A. (2006). The decline of the raven, *Corvus corax*, in relation to afforestation in southern Scotland and northern England. *Journal of Applied Ecology*, **15**:129–144.

218   Pearce-Higgins, J.W., Grant, M.C., Robinson, M.C. & Haysom, S.L. (2007). The role of forest maturation in causing the decline of Black Grouse *Tetrao tetrix*. *Ibis*, **149**:143–155.

219   Douglas, D.J.T., Bellamy, P.E., Stephen, L.S., Pearce-Higgins, J.W., Wilson, J.D. & Grant, M.C. (2014). Upland land use predicts population decline in a globally near-threatened wader. *Journal of Applied Ecology*, **51**:194–203.

220   Newton, I. (1986). Principles underlying bird numbers in Scottish woodlands. In: *Trees and Wildlife in the Scottish Uplands*: (ed. Jenkins, D.) NERC/ITE. Banchory.

221   Cayford, J.T. (1990). Distribution and habitat preferences of black grouse in commercial forests in Wales: conservation and management implications. In: *Proceedings of the International Union of Game Biologists Congress*: 435–447.

222   Reynolds, B. & Edwards, A. (1995). Factors influencing dissolved nitrogen concentrations and loadings in upland streams of the UK. *Agricultural Water Management*, **27**:181–202.

223   Worrall, F., Chapman, P., Holden, J., Evans, C., Artz, R., Smith, P. & Grayson, R. (2011). A review of current evidence on carbon fluxes and greenhouse gas emissions from UK peatlands. *JNCC report 442*. Peterborough.

224 Lavers, C.P. & Haines-Young, R.H. (1997). Displacement of dunlin *Calidris alpina schinzii* by forestry in the flow country and an estimate of the value of moorland adjacent to plantations. *Biological Conservation*, **79**:87–90.

225 Scottish Renewables. Renewables in Numbers. Available at: https://www.scottishrenewables.com/forums/renewables-in-numbers/.

226 Pearce-Higgins, J.W., Stephen, L., Douse, A. & Langston, R.H.W. (2012). Greater impacts of wind farms on bird populations during construction than subsequent operation: Results of a multi-site and multi-species analysis. *Journal of Applied Ecology*, **49**:386–394.

227 The Scottish Government. The Less Favoured Area Support Scheme (Scotland) Amendment Regulations 2019: EQIA. 2019: Available at: https://www.gov.scot/publications/less-favoured-area-support-scheme-scotland-amendment-regulations-2019-eqia/.

228 Bardgett, R.D., Marsden, J.H. & Howard, D.C. (1995). The extent and condition of heather on moorland in the uplands of England and Wales. *Biological Conservation*, **71**:155–161.

229 Dunlop, S. (2010). *An Economic Study of Grouse Moors*.

Join the GWCT

Make sure you never miss the latest news and events by joining the GWCT

As a member of the Trust you will not only be helping to fund the scientific research, you'll be the first to hear about it.

What you receive when you become a GWCT member:

- Priority access to dozens of unique courses and events taking place throughout the year.
- Free copies of Gamewise, our feature-packed magazine produced three times a year.
- Your own copy of our annual Review.
- An invitation to the GWCT's Scottish Game Fair at Scone Palace.
- Regular email updates containing all our latest news and research findings.
- Membership of your local county group and invitations to events in your area.
- Pleasure from the knowledge that you're helping the British countryside thrive both now and in the future.

Call us today on **01425 652381** or visit **www.gwct.org.uk/join**

Have you got The Knowledge?

Whether you're new to shooting, a seasoned gun or just keen to learn more about the way the British countryside is managed, The Knowledge is for you. Featuring over 200 pages of easy-to-read questions and answers such as:

- How do you define a wild pheasant?
- Why are grey partridges on the quarry list when they are in national decline?
- Why do gamebirds need supplementary food?
- Does predation control have wider conservation benefits?
- What UK habitats do woodcock prefer?
- What should Guns look out for on a shoot day?

The Knowledge draws on over 150 scientific publications to provide you with a robust introduction into quarry species, the management of both habitat and predators and all the latest issues surrounding shooting and conservation. You will also learn key information about a typical day's shooting – from important health & safety tips to guidance on game handling and security. Featuring a new foreword by bushcraft expert Ray Mears, The Knowledge is essential for all those who want to know more about shooting and conservation.

Order your copy today at www.gwctshop.org.uk

𝕏 🅵 🅾 ▶ gwct.org.uk

Game & Wildlife
CONSERVATION TRUST